P9-CRA-294

Microbiology
Lab Manual
SECOND EDITION

Roger Lightner • Joshua Burns

Kendall Hunt
publishing company

Cover image © Shutterstock.com

Kendall Hunt
publishing company

www.kendallhunt.com
Send all inquiries to:
4050 Westmark Drive
Dubuque, IA 52004-1840

Copyright © 2018, 2020 by Kendall Hunt Publishing Company

ISBN: 978-1-7924-2486-1

All rights reserved. No part of this publication may be reproduced,
stored in a retrieval system, or transmitted, in any form or by any means,
electronic, mechanical, photocopying, recording, or otherwise,
without the prior written permission of the copyright owner.

Published in the United States of America

Table of Contents

Preface

This microbiology lab manual is designed for the General Microbiology lab at the University of Arkansas Fort Smith. This lab is taken by a diverse group of students. The procedures included in this manual should give health science majors the basic background in laboratory techniques that they will need in their future programs and careers. At the same time, we have included material that will train biology majors with valuable skills to prepare them for upper level biology classes while gaining an understanding of the microbial world around them. Most labs will contain material they will perform on day one and then record results of their experiments following incubation on day two when they return the following week.

The laboratory portion of each course is designed to complement the lecture. In lecture, the concepts and procedures will be introduced and then the laboratory period allows students to get hands-on training that will help students obtain a more thorough understanding of the concepts and techniques involved.

These laboratory courses are introductory level so the labs are constructed to minimize the risk of coming in contact with dangerous chemicals or microorganisms. Cultures used in the lab are relatively harmless and safe for beginning students to handle. The lab, however, does inherently contain minimal risks because of the materials that will be handled, and this can vary depending on each student's personal condition of health, such as being immunocompromised. These issues will be addressed in the next section on laboratory safety guidelines that will be covered on the first day of lab.

Mr. Roger Lightner
Biology Instructor, University of Arkansas Fort Smith

Laboratory Safety Guidelines

1. A microbiology laboratory does not have as many hazards as a chemistry lab. However, there will be times when we handle materials that require some personal protective equipment (PPE). Goggles and gloves are provided in the lab, and your instructor will demonstrate during each lab period what materials are necessary to complete the work.

2. You should begin and end each period by disinfecting your tabletop and washing your hands. This will prevent contamination of your experiment and clean up after your own work as a courtesy to the next student who will sit in your spot.

3. During most of the labs, we will be using the Bunsen burner. This is an open flame, so books and coats should be placed in a safe location. Long hair should be tied back. Some labs will require the use of alcohol, so special care should be taken to keep the flammable liquid away from the open flame. The burner should be turned off when not in use because it is a source of unnecessary heat.

4. The cultures we will handle in this introductory lab are safe for beginning students to work with. However, a person who is immunocompromised, pregnant, or taking immunosuppressant drugs could still be vulnerable. Please notify your instructor if one of these conditions applies to you.

5. While working in the lab, you should never touch your face, apply cosmetics, or adjust contact lenses.

6. Materials should not be removed from the lab without instructor permission.

7. No food or drink should be brought into the laboratory.

8. Pipetting aids are provided, so no mouth pipetting is allowed.

9. The proper dress for lab should include shorts or skirts that go at least to the knee and closed toed shoes. No flip-flops or open sandals should be worn.

10. Report any accidents or spills to the instructor immediately for assistance in cleaning up a spill. Materials that come into contact with cultures should be placed in a biohazard container, and broken glass or sharp objects should be placed in a sharps container.

11. Test tubes should be placed into a rack to hold them. The tops are not liquid tight, and they can rolloff of the table when laid down on their side.

12. You should read over each week's lab before class to be prepared. You should also never rush through your lab. Getting in a hurry will only lead to mistakes.

13. After using the microscope, you must wipe off the oil from the 100× objective lens to prevent damage to the scope. Your microscope slide can be disposed of in the sharps container on each desk.

14. Please sign and date the following first copy of the form to show that you have read, understand, and intend to comply with all safety guidelines for this lab. Tear out the sheet and turn it in to your instructor. There is a second copy for your own reference starting on the following page. You are now ready to perform labs safely. I hope you enjoy your laboratory experience.

Printed Name: _____

Signature: _____   Date: _____

Laboratory Safety Guidelines

1. A microbiology laboratory does not have as many hazards as a chemistry lab. However, there will be times when we handle materials that require some personal protective equipment (PPE). Goggles and gloves are provided in the lab and your instructor will demonstrate during each lab period what materials are necessary to complete the work.

2. You should begin and end each period by disinfecting your tabletop and washing your hands. This will prevent contamination of your experiment and clean up after your own work as a courtesy to the next student who will sit in your spot.

3. During most of the labs, we will be using the Bunsen burner. This is an open flame, so books and coats should be placed in a safe location. Long hair should be tied back. Some labs will require the use of alcohol so special care should be taken to keep the flammable liquid away from the open flame. The burner should be turned off when not in use because it is a source of unnecessary heat.

4. The cultures we will handle in this introductory lab are safe for beginning students to work with. However, a person who is immunocompromised, pregnant, or taking immunosuppressant drugs could still be vulnerable. Please notify your instructor if one of these conditions applies to you.

5. While working in the lab, you should never touch your face, apply cosmetics, or adjust contact lenses.

6. Materials should not be removed from the lab without instructor permission.

7. No food or drink should be brought into the laboratory.

8. Pipetting aids are provided so no mouth pipetting is allowed.

9. The proper dress for lab should include shorts or skirts that go at least to the knee and closed toed shoes. No flip-flops or open sandals should be worn.

10. Report any accidents or spills to the instructor immediately for assistance in cleaning up a spill. Materials that come into contact with cultures should be placed in a biohazard container, and broken glass or sharp objects should be placed in a sharps container.

11. Test tubes should be placed into a rack to hold them. The tops are not liquid tight, and they can rolloff of the table when laid down on their side.

12. You should read over each week's lab before class to be prepared. You should also never rush through your lab. Getting in a hurry will only lead to mistakes.

13. After using the microscope, you must wipe off the oil from the 100× objective lens to prevent damage to the scope. Your microscope slide can be disposed of in the sharps container on each desk.

14. Please sign and date the first copy of the form to show that you have read, understand, and intend to comply with all safety guidelines for this lab. Tear out the sheet and turn it in to your instructor. Retain the second copy for your own reference. You are now ready to perform labs safely. I hope you enjoy your laboratory experience.

Student Copy

"Pet" Identification Form

Student Name: _____

Letter Identification of "Pet": _____

A. Microscopy
   1. Gram Stain: _____
   2. Cell Shape: _____
   3. Cell Arrangements: _____
   4. Endospores?: _____

B. Environmental Conditions
   1. Temperature: _____
   2. pH: _____
   3. Halotolerance?: _____
   4. Oxygen: _____

C. Selective Media
   1. Colony Morphology on TSA: _____
   2. Mannitol Salt Agar (MSA): _____
   3. Eosin Methylene Blue (EMB) Agar: _____
   4. MacConkey (MAC) Agar: _____

D. Differential Biochemical Tests
   1. Phenol Red Broth – Carbohydrate Fermentation
      a. Glucose/Dextrose: _____
      b. Lactose: _____
      c. Glycerol: _____
      d. Mannitol: _____
   2. IMViC Series
      a. Tryptone Broth – Indole: _____
      b. MRVP Broth – Methyl Red: _____
      c. Citrate Agar: _____
   3. Additional Tests
      a. Nitrate: _____
      b. Starch: _____
      c. TSI – H_2S: _____
      d. Gelatin: _____
      e. Bile Esculin: _____
      f. Motility Test: _____
      g. Oxidase: _____

Student Identification of "Pet" (Genus and Species): _____

Dichotomous Key for Pet Bacteria

I. Bacterium is Gram Positive
    A. Cells are Rod shaped (Bacilli)
        1. Culture is positive for endospores   *Bacillus cereus*
        2. Culture is negative for endospores   *Lactobacillus acidophilus*

    B. Cells are Coccus shaped
        1. Cell arrangement is clusters
            a. Culture is halotolerant and gives a fuchsia growth on MSA   *Staphylococcus epidermidis*
            b. Culture is halotolerant and gives a yellow growth on MSA   *Staphylococcus aureus*

        2. Cell arrangement is chains
            a. Culture is not halotolerant, does not grow well on MSA, +BEA   *Enterococcus faecalis*
            b. Culture is not halotolerant, does not grow well on MSA, -BEA   *Streptococcus lactis*

II. Bacterium is Gram Negative
    A. Cells are Rod shaped (Bacilli)
        1. Culture is aerobic from Thioglycolate or oxidase positive   *Alcaligenes faecalis*
        2. Culture is facultative anaerobe on Thioglycolate or oxidase negative
            a. Culture is positive for lactose fermentation and gas production
                i. Culture is + Citrate, - Methyl Red, - Indole   *Enterobacter aerogenes*
                ii. Culture is - Citrate, + Methyl Red, + Indole, green sheen   *Escherichia coli*
            b. Culture is negative for lactose fermentation and +H2S   *Proteus vulgaris*

    B. Cells are Coccus shaped   These are extremely rare!

Source: Roger Lightner

Pet ID Flow Chart

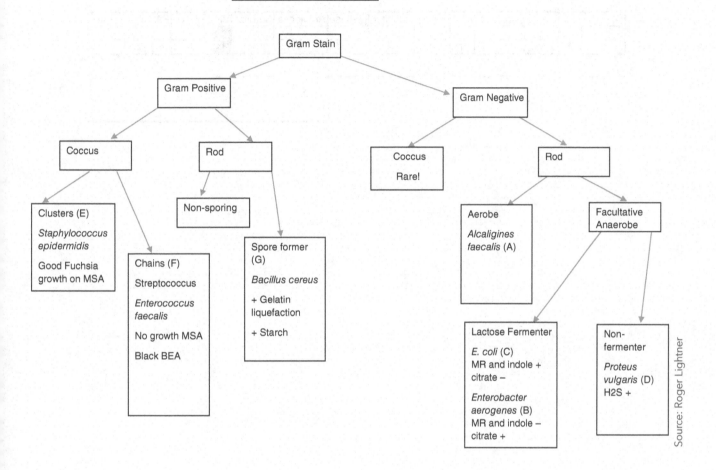

Gram Stain

Gram Positive → Coccus, Rod

Gram Negative → Coccus (Rare!), Rod

Coccus:
- Clusters (E)
  Staphylococcus epidermidis
  Good Fuchsia growth on MSA
- Chains (F)
  Streptococcus
  Enterococcus faecalis
  No growth MSA
  Black BEA

Rod (Gram Positive):
- Non-sporing
- Spore former (G)
  Bacillus cereus
  + Gelatin liquefaction
  + Starch

Rod (Gram Negative):
- Aerobe
  Alcaligines faecalis (A)
- Facultative Anaerobe
  - Lactose Fermenter
    E. coli (C)
    MR and indole +
    citrate –

    Enterobacter aerogenes (B)
    MR and indole –
    citrate +
  - Non-fermenter
    Proteus vulgaris (D)
    H2S +

Source: Roger Lightner

Enteropluri Test

Sample: _____

Glucose	Gas	Lysine	Ornithine	H2S	Indole	Adonitol	Lactose	Arabinose	Sorbitol	VP	Dulcitol	PA	Urea	Citrate
2	1	4	2	1	4	2	1	4	2	■	1	4	2	1

_____   _____   _____   _____   _____   _____

_____

Source: Roger Lightner

LAB WEEK

1

Microbiological Media and Culturing of Microorganisms

DAY 1: INTRODUCTION TO MEDIA AND CULTURING

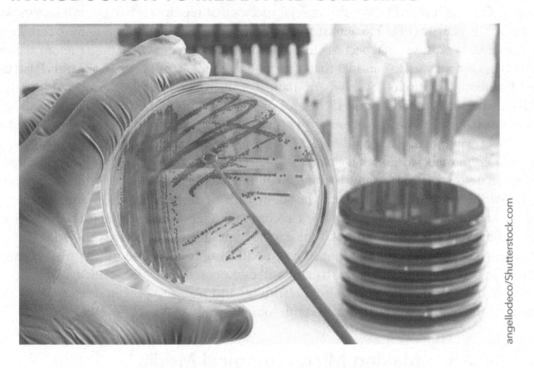

angellodeco/Shutterstock.com

Several individuals in history that you will gradually learn about in this course are responsible for one of the most important discoveries of science known as the **Germ Theory of Disease**. This Germ Theory states that many common diseases are caused by microorganisms and can be contagious and spread by contact (direct or indirect) with infected persons. Once these microbes were discovered, there was a need to grow them artificially in a laboratory setting for further studies. The first person to grow bacteria artificially in a lab was **Robert Koch**. In the late 1800s, he was trying to diagnose the cause of anthrax, a potentially fatal disease of domestic livestock that can infect humans when they come into contact with the diseased animals. Koch was able to isolate the bacterium *Bacillus anthracis* on an artificial medium. **Media** are the substances that contain all the nutrients an organism needs to grow. A medium can come in the form of a solid agar in a Petri dish or a broth in a test tube or a flask. Koch realized that he needed a solid medium to spread the bacteria away from each other to isolate the causative agent into a pure culture or single species by itself. Later, he was able to illustrate that this species caused the disease by injecting the pure culture into a healthy animal and it coming down with the disease. Thus, Robert Koch was the first person to diagnose the cause of a particular disease and develop these isolation techniques. During the process of developing this solid medium, Koch became frustrated trying to find the right material. He first tried potato slices and gelatin, but it did not work very well. The wife of one of his graduate assistants named **Angelina Hess** suggested the use of **agar,** which is an extract from seaweed that is used as a thickening agent. Agar is an inert substance that solidifies the medium, but is usually not consumed by the microbes, allowing the medium to remain solid even at the incubation temperature required for animals and humans. Below you can make a list of ingredients that must be supplied in a medium in order for common microbes to grow.

There are different types of media with different specific functions you will be exposed to throughout the semester. The most common medium used in this lab is called **Tryptic Soy Agar (TSA)** or **Tryptic Soy Broth (TSB)**. This is a soy bean–based medium that provides protein to promote good bacterial growth. TSA is an example of a complex medium in which the exact chemical makeup is not known in detail and can vary slightly from batch to batch. Occasionally, a defined medium in which the exact chemical composition is known may be required to identify the specific nutritional requirements for a particular organism. One exercise today involves inoculating a defined medium called **Glucose Minimal Salts (GMS) agar**. This medium will identify bacterial species that require certain growth factors. We will also use **Potato Dextrose agar (PDA)** to demonstrate that different types of microbes have certain preferences in their nutrients. We can see that bacteria like high **protein** sources, while fungi prefer **carbohydrate**.

The next person we need to consider that contributed to the Germ Theory was **Louis Pasteur**. He demonstrated the ubiquitous (found everywhere) nature of microbes when he performed his famous **swan-necked flask** experiment that debunked the idea of **Spontaneous Generation**. Today, you will inoculate one agar plate by touching various objects from the environment around you and you should see growth from any object you touch. Also, on this plate, you will have a control section. Scientists run controlled experiments to remove biases and make sure that their materials are working properly. The purpose of the control section on this plate is to show that the medium is sterile and that the cotton swabs you will be using are also sterile. This means any growth you see on the rest of the plate is from the object you touched.

One last concept to learn today is aseptic technique. **Aseptic technique** is all the little maneuvers you make to prevent contamination of your experiment and cultures. This includes using a Bunsen burner to sterilize your inoculating loop. The **inoculating loop** is one of the most commonly used instruments in this laboratory. Your instructor will demonstrate how to sterilize it by getting it red hot in the Bunsen burner and also how to hold test tubes and plates to prevent contamination. Now you have enough information to start your first microbiology lab.

Exercise #1   Making Microbiological Media

Procedure #1 – Mixing Media

- Work as a group at your table.
- Pour the premeasured TSA powder from the weigh boat into the flask.
- Add 250 ml of deionized (DI) water to the flask and swirl to mix a little.
- Cap the flask with a square of aluminum foil.
- Your instructor will sterilize this in an autoclave to be used later.

Procedure #2 – Pouring Agar Plates

- Obtain a sterile flask of molten agar for the group already prepared from the water bath.
- Each student should write their initials on the bottom of an empty Petri dish with a sharpie.

- Each student should take a turn pouring agar into their empty Petri dish.
- Pour enough agar to cover the bottom of the dish and allow to sit still until hardened.
- These plates will be stored for you to use next week and check for contamination.

Exercise #2   Enriching for Microbes with Specific Nutrients

Procedure – Ubiquitous Nature of Microorganisms

- Each student should obtain one TSA plate and one PDA plate. Label these plates as you pick them up because they look so similar to each other.
- Using a sharpie, divide the bottom of each plate into four pie sections and label as shown in the following diagram.
- For the control section, you will get a sterile cotton swab and swab the surface of the agar in that section. Use the same swab to touch both plates.
- For the remaining three pie sections, you will touch various objects of your choice with a sterile cotton swab and then touch both the plates in the properly labeled section. Examples include money, cell phones, door knobs, and so on.
- After the plates are labeled, place them in the designated area for the instructor to incubate until next week.

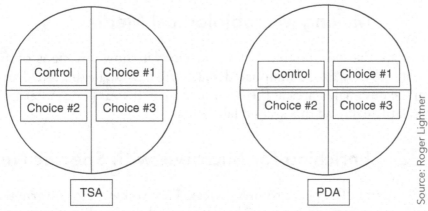

Labeling Instructions for Environmental Swab Plates

Source: Roger Lightner

Exercise #3   Complex versus Defined Media

GMS agar is a defined medium. It has just some basic minerals that most living organisms need and glucose is the only carbohydrate source. Each ingredient is exactly known, so this is what makes it defined. It has no vitamins. For a species to grow on this medium, it has to produce everything it needs from the glucose. If it is not able to do so, it will not grow. Your instructor will provide four different bacterial cultures in test tubes and demonstrate the aseptic technique you will use to transfer each culture to the agar plates to perform a **spot inoculation**. If a culture grows on the TSA but not the GMS, this means it requires a **growth factor** such as a vitamin that is not provided by the GMS medium.

Procedure – Glucose Minimal Salts Agar versus Tryptic Soy Agar

- Each table should obtain one GMS plate and one TSA plate.
- Label the plates as shown in the following diagram.

- Spot inoculate each of the four cultures onto each of the plates by sterilizing the inoculating loop in the Bunsen burner between each culture and making about 1 cm long streaks in each pie section with a loop full of culture.
- Place all plates in the designated area for the instructor to incubate until next week.

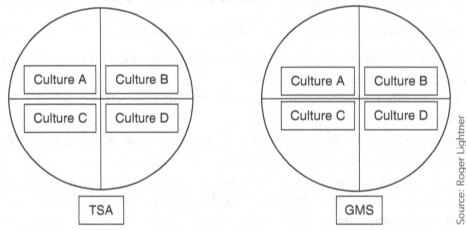

Labeling Instructions for the Media Comparison Plates

Source: Roger Lightner

DAY 2: RESULTS

Exercise #1   Making Microbiological Media

Observe your plate that you poured last week. Does it show any signs of growth? Your plate should be sterile with no growth. Contaminated plates will need to be discarded and you can obtain a replacement from the designated area at the front of the lab. If your plate is sterile, you may use it for your isolation streak plate during this second lab period.

Exercise #2   Enriching for Microbes with Specific Nutrients

Observe your TSA and PDA plates from last week. First you want to confirm that the control section of each plate does not contain any growth. Next, you should notice that the other three sections should have growth. The growth in each section will not be identical because different organisms grow in different environments, but there should be something in each area showing the ubiquitous nature of microorganisms. Lastly, compare the colonies from the TSA plate to the ones on the PDA plate. Bacterial colonies are usually shiny, smooth, and creamy. Fungal colonies are usually fuzzy in appearance. Which plate has more fungal colonies on it? Today we will only be working with bacterial colonies.

Last week you inoculated plates by swabbing items from the environment and then touching the plates with the cotton swab to introduce the microbes to the medium. These plates have been incubating for a week to allow the microorganisms to grow. You cannot see the individual cells with the naked eye, but most of these organisms reproduce asexually by a simple cell division. Over time as these cell numbers increase, it produces a visible growth called a **colony**. Each species can produce colonies with unique physical characteristics that can aid in their identification. The study of the shape and texture of these colonies is called **colony morphology**. The following diagram demonstrates the commonly used terms that we use to describe these colonies. First, making a note of what color the colony produces can be an important characteristic. Next, we look at the **form** or shape of the whole colony. **Circular** or round colonies are quite common. Sometimes, these round colonies are so small that they just look like pin dots and are said to be **punctiform**. If the colony looks more random, we say it is **irregular** in shape. Some colonies are more **filamentous** or stringy. Colonies can also vary in their **surface** texture. Some are **entirely smooth** and glisten. Others have a **rough** texture that can be extreme enough to look like mountain **ridges**. The outer **edge** or margin of the colony can also vary. This edge can be **smooth** or have an **undulating** appearance like a serrated knife blade. **Lobate** colonies have obvious rounded lobes diverging from the edge. Lastly, the **elevation** of the colony is considered. This refers to the height or thickness of the colony from the surface of the agar. Many colonies are **convex** like domed stadiums or so **flat** they seem to have no height at all. **Raised** colonies have obvious thickness, but the top surface is variable in texture. Use these terms to fill in the results table below. You should describe at least three different-looking colonies so you can practice with as many terms as possible.

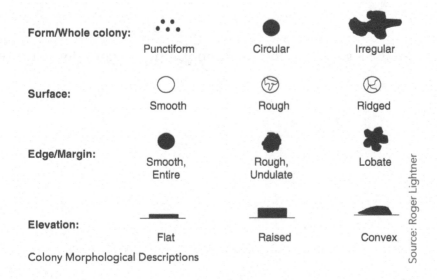

Colony Morphological Descriptions

Source: Roger Lightner

Colony Morphology

Colony #	Color	Form	Surface	Edge	Elevation
1					
2					
3					

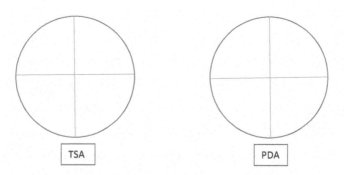

Use this figure to make drawings of what the growth you got on your TSA and PDA plates looks like to you.

Exercise #3   Complex versus Defined Media

In the following table, record whether each culture grew or not on each medium. Use a (+) to designate growth and a (−) to designate no growth.

Growth Requirement Comparison

Culture	TSA	GMS
A		
B		
C		
D		

Which organisms require a growth factor? Which organism is known for not requiring growth factors?

1. Who was the first person to isolate and culture bacteria in a laboratory setting?
   a. Robert Hooke
   b. Robert Koch
   c. Louis Pasteur
   d. Joseph Lister
   e. Edward Jenner

2. Who demonstrated the ubiquitous nature of microbes by performing his famous "swan-necked flask" experiment?
   a. Robert Hooke
   b. Robert Koch
   c. Louis Pasteur
   d. Joseph Lister
   e. Edward Jenner

3. What is the purpose of adding agar to a medium?
   a. it serves as a carbon source
   b. it serves as a nitrogen source
   c. it serves as a source of vitamins
   d. it serves as a solidifying agent.

4. TSA is the most common medium in a microbiological lab and is classified as a _____ medium.
   a. complex
   b. defined

5. Bacteria prefer food sources that are high in _____.
   a. carbohydrate
   b. protein

6. Which medium should have more fungal colonies growing on it?
   a. TSA
   b. PDA

7. The control section of the plate from Exercise #2 should contain growth.
   a. true
   b. false

8. Fats and carbohydrates are added to media to serve as sources of:
   a. carbon and energy
   b. protein
   c. sulfur
   d. enzymes

9. A nitrogen source in the medium is important so that the organism can produce:
   a. carbohydrate
   b. fat
   c. protein
   d. vitamins

10. Vitamins and minerals are important ingredients in media because organisms can use them as:
    a. energy sources
    b. protein sources
    c. sources of phosphorus
    d. coenzymes and cofactors

2

Isolation Streak, Microscope, and Simple Stain

DAY 1: ISOLATION AND STAINING

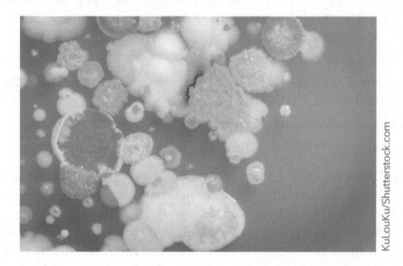

KuLouKu/Shutterstock.com

Now that you have learned how to prepare media for growing a variety of microorganisms, we will next discuss how to isolate them. An isolation streak plate is a technique used to get one species of bacteria by itself in what is called a **pure culture**. We usually work with pure cultures in the laboratory so that we know which traits and characteristics can be assigned to which organism. Last week, we talked about Robert Koch. He realized that in order to isolate the organism that caused anthrax, he would need a solid medium so that he could spread the bacteria away from each other. The following diagram shows how an isolation streak plate is performed to illustrate the concept.

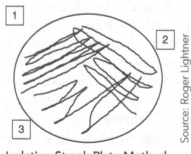

Source: Roger Lightner

Isolation Streak Plate Method

Exercise #1 Isolating Bacteria into Pure Cultures

Procedure – Isolation Streak Plate

- Hold your inoculation loop like a pencil and sterilize it in the Bunsen burner by getting the shaft of the wire red hot in the flame. Migrate the wire up out of the flame until the entire wire and loop have become red hot.

- Let the loop cool for a few seconds so it does not kill the bacteria when you touch them. If you hear a sizzle, you will know the loop is still too hot.

- Touch the loop to a colony of your choice from a plate from last week. Just scrape a tiny bit onto the loop. You will notice most bacterial colonies have a consistency similar to mayonnaise. You do not need a big glob hanging from your loop.

- On a new sterile plate, touch the plate with the loop and streak back and forth over about one-third of the plate's surface to inoculate the material.

- Sterilize the loop a second time in the Bunsen burner.

- With a sterile loop, touch the area of the plate where your first streak is to pick up a small amount of that material and then drag to the clean area to make more streaks over a second one-third of the plate to drag the cells away from each other.

- Sterilize the loop a third time in the Bunsen burner.

- To make sure we get separation, you repeat this by performing a third streak over the rest of the plate after touching the second streak.

- Sterilize the loop a final time to remove any contamination before putting it away.

- Label your isolation streak plate and place it in the designated area for incubation until next week.

The last thing you will do today is prepare a microscope slide so that you can see what the individual bacterial cells from a colony look like. But first, we need to cover the basics of how to use a microscope and learn its parts. When you get your microscope out of the cabinet, you will want to carry it with two hands to prevent dropping it. You should grab it by the **body tube** with one hand and then support the **base** with the other hand. When you set the microscope down on a surface, do it gently because the optics are fragile. Next, you can remove the large power plug from the back of the microscope and plug it into an outlet. Now, let us take a tour of the microscope and see what the function of each part is. There is a labeled picture on the next page to help you find the parts.

The lenses you look into at the top of the microscope are called **ocular lenses** or eyepieces. They are usually 10x in magnification. These microscopes have two oculars (one for each eye) and are therefore called **binocular** microscopes. You will notice the ocular lens can be adjusted for your eye width and focused separately to correct for individual vision.

Next, locate the **revolving nosepiece** that will have four **objective lenses** hanging from it. Each of these lenses has a different power of magnification and works with the ocular lens to determine the total magnification of your specimen. To calculate **total magnification,** you multiply the power of the ocular lens and the objective lens you are using. Total magnification is summarized in the table in the results section at the end of this lab. The 4x objective is called the **scanning lens** because it is very low power, and you use it to properly line up your specimen on the stage and locate it in the field of view. The 10x objective is called the **low power lens** and allows you to find your specimen with enough magnification to observe initial characteristics about it. The 40x objective is called the **high-dry lens** because there will not be any liquid present while it is used. This lens allows you to see specimens at higher magnification but does get a little blurry. Lastly, these scopes have a 100x **oil-immersion lens** present. This lens will be necessary to observe bacteria because they are so small. Microscopes are **parfocal**, which means that if you are in focus with one objective, it will be very close to being in focus when you rotate to the next higher power. With the scope in as good of focus as you can manage with the 40x objective, you will rotate it out of the way and place a drop of immersion oil on the microscope slide. Next, you will rotate the 100x lens right into the oil and fine focus. The image of your specimen should be much clearer now, and you should see individual bacterial cells. Remember to wipe the oil off of the lens with lens paper when you are finished.

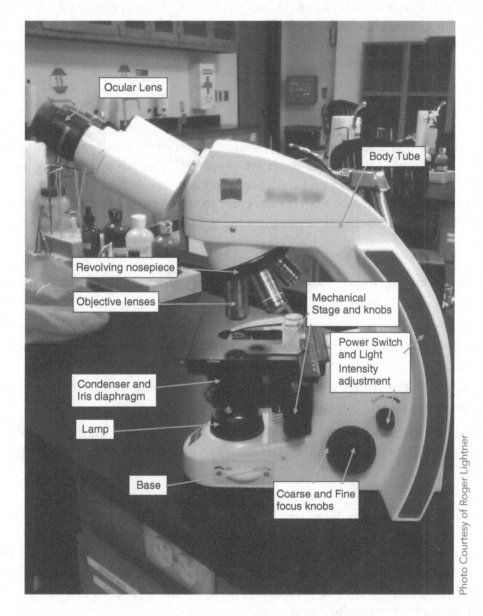

Ocular Lens

Body Tube

Revolving nosepiece

Objective lenses

Mechanical Stage and knobs

Power Switch and Light Intensity adjustment

Condenser and Iris diaphragm

Lamp

Base

Coarse and Fine focus knobs

Photo Courtesy of Roger Lightner

The flat portion of the microscope where your microscope slide is placed is called the **stage**. There is a stage clip that will support your slide. Attached to the stage clip are knobs that allow you to move your slide around for proper alignment. All of the moving components are called the **mechanical stage**. You will want to position your microscope slide so that your specimen is lined up where the light is coming up through the stage to the objective lens.

Underneath the stage is the **condenser lens**. This lens focuses the light from the lamp on the slide to give good illumination for the specimen. On the front of the condenser is a lever for the **iris diaphragm**, which opens and closes like a camera shutter to adjust the level of illumination.

The **lamp** or light source is located at the bottom of the scope and shines light up toward the objective lenses. These scopes have a **power switch** on the side. When you turn the switch, you will feel it click on; if you keep turning it, the lamp gets brighter so the switch also functions as a **light intensity adjustment**. You will also notice some LED lights on the side of the scope that light up gradually to give you a relative indication of where the light intensity is set. The more lights lit up means the brighter the lamp is.

The large focus knobs on the side of the microscope have a wheel-within-a-wheel design. The larger outer wheel is the **coarse focus knob**. When you turn it, you will notice that the stage moves up and down rapidly for getting close to being in focus quickly. The smaller, inner wheel is the **fine focus knob**. This knob moves the stage vertically very slowly for fine tuning to get the specimen in as clear focus as possible at each magnification.

Exercise #2   Bacterial Smears

Now that you have had a tour of the microscope, you are ready to prepare your first bacterial smear to view in the scope. Most of the slides we prepare in this lab are dry smears that are then stained. Bacterial cells are very small and transparent so they are difficult to see in the microscope. They are usually stained with a dye of a fairly dark color to create **contrast** and make them more easily viewed. The following are the steps for preparing a bacterial smear:

Procedure – Preparing a Bacterial Smear

- Use your inoculating loop to place a small drop of water in the middle of a clean microscope slide.
- Sterilize your inoculating loop in the Bunsen burner.
- Touch one of the colonies from your agar plate from last week's lab that looks most interesting to you. All you need is a little bacteria to stick to your loop; if you scrape off a big blob, your smear will be too thick.
- Smear the bacteria in the drop of water on the slide and spread it around to get it as thin as possible.
- Let the smear air dry or dry on a slide warmer.
- Heat fix the slide by passing the slide gently three or four times over the Bunsen burner. Heat fixing makes the bacterial cells stick to the glass better so they do not wash away during the staining procedure.

Exercise #3   Simple Stains

Today you will perform a simple stain for your first stain. A **simple stain** means that only one color is used. This stain will not provide much information about the specimen but will let you see the size, shape, and arrangement of the bacterial cells. This stain will be a good practice run for performing a more detailed staining procedure next week.

Procedure – Performing a Simple Stain

- Your instructor will show you a tip on how to label your slide to remember which side is the top where the bacteria are located. If you ever get your slide upside down, your stain will not turn out properly.
- Place your slide down flat on a piece of paper towel and flood it with crystal violet stain for 1 minute.
- Use a water bottle to rinse the excess stain gently off of the slide by flushing it into the sink.
- Use a book of bibulous paper to blot the excess water off between the sheets.

Tips for Focusing on Your Specimen

- Place the slide into the slide holder of the microscope with the stained smear facing up.
- Use the mechanical stage to place the colored smear over the light coming up through the condenser with the microscope turned on.
- Start with the 4x objective in place and the stage all the way down.
- While looking through the ocular lenses, slowly bring the stage up with the coarse focus knob until you start to see the color come into focus.
- Now switch to the fine focus knob and slowly adjust to get the smear as clear as possible.
- Rotate the 10x objective in place and refocus with the fine focus knob. The smear should look larger, but the bacterial cells still look like little pin dots.
- Rotate the 40x objective in place and refocus as best you can with the fine focus knob. Do not worry if it is a little blurry; just get it as close as possible.
- Rotate the revolving nosepiece halfway between the 40x and 100x objective lenses and use the dipstick to place a drop of immersion oil on the slide where the light is coming up through.
- Rotate the 100x objective in place. It is designed to get very close to the slide without touching it, and the oil will displace the air and form a seal around the lens. When you fine focus, the image should be crystal clear now.
- When finished viewing, remove your slide from the scope and discard it in the sharps container on the desk. Put the stage all the way down and rotate the 4x objective in place to keep the stage and objectives from crashing into each other. Use a sheet of lens paper to wipe the oil off of the 100x objective and put your scope away.

DAY 1: RESULTS

Total Magnification

Objective Lens	Ocular Lens	Total Magnification
Scanning lens (4x)	10x	
Low power lens (10x)	10x	
High-dry lens (40x)	10x	
Oil-immersion lens (100x)	10x	

Use this figure to make a drawing of what your bacterium looked like from the simple stain

Source: Roger Lightner

DAY 2: RESULTS

Use this figure to make a drawing of what your isolation streak plate looks like after incubating since last week

Source: Roger Lightner

1. If a bacterial colony has an elevation like a dome, it is said to be:
   a. flat
   b. raised
   c. convex
   d. filamentous

2. Fungal colonies can usually be distinguished from bacterial colonies because fungal colonies are usually:
   a. fuzzy
   b. creamy

3. When performing an isolation streak plate, which streak is performed after touching the bacterial colony from the original plate?
   a. first streak only
   b. second streak only
   c. third streak only
   d. this is done for all streaks

4. Which microscope part allows you to change magnification by changing objective lenses?
   a. iris diaphragm
   b. mechanical stage
   c. revolving nosepiece
   d. coarse focus knob

5. Which microscope part moves the specimen around?
   a. iris diaphragm
   b. mechanical stage
   c. revolving nosepiece
   d. coarse focus knob

6. Which microscope part adjusts the brightness of the specimen?
   a. iris diaphragm
   b. mechanical stage
   c. revolving nosepiece
   d. coarse focus knob

7. Which focus knob moves the stage more rapidly?
   a. coarse focus
   b. fine focus

8. What is the total magnification of a specimen if the 10x objective lens is in position?
   a. 10x
   b. 20x
   c. 100x
   d. 1,000x

9. Which objective lens should be in position while transporting the microscope?

    a. 4x

    b. 10x

    c. 40x

    d. 100x

10. Which objective lens is also known as the high-dry lens?

    a. 4x

    b. 10x

    c. 40x

    d. 100x

3

Differential Stains: Gram Stain

DAY 1: GRAM STAIN

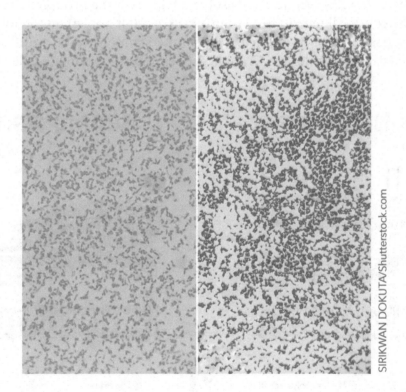

SIRIKWAN DOKUTA/Shutterstock.com

Last week you learned how to prepare a bacterial smear and perform a simple stain. You also learned how to use the microscope properly and focus on a bacterial smear with oil immersion. This week you will perform a more complex staining procedure called the Gram stain. The **Gram stain** is probably the most well-known stain in microbiology and an example of a differential staining technique. Simple stains only allow you to see the size and shape of each cell more clearly. **Differential stains** allow you to distinguish between types of cells or cell parts because chemical reactions will cause different structures to stain different colors.

The Gram stain differentiates between the two main groups of bacteria based on their cell wall structure. The staining technique was developed in 1884 by **Hans Christian Gram**. He accidentally stumbled upon the results while performing differential stains of human lung tissue. Gram was trying to get the bacteria to stain more obviously so they could be seen among the human cells, but he noticed that the bacteria themselves would turn out different colors. We now know this is due largely to the thickness of the cell wall material called peptidoglycan.

The following diagram illustrates the basic difference between what we call Gram-positive and Gram-negative cell wall structure. Gram-positive cell walls are thicker with multiple layers of a strong but porous peptidoglycan located right outside the cell membrane. Gram-negative cells have thin (usually a single layer) peptidoglycan walls with a second membrane outside of that called an **outer membrane**. The thickness or number of layers of peptidoglycan is key to how the Gram stain works. Consider peptidoglycan as being like a chain-linked fence, which is very strong but very porous. The first stain used in the Gram stain procedure is crystal violet. This is followed with an application of iodine, which reacts with the crystal violet to form a precipitate that is insoluble in water. Now consider this precipitate as being like tennis balls stuck between layers of chain-linked fence in a Gram-positive cell. The tennis balls would be stuck very tight and hard to remove. However, a Gram-negative cell would be like having one layer of fence with tennis balls stuck in it that could be pushed out and removed fairly easily. This is what happens during the third step of the technique. The precipitate is not soluble in water, but during the third step, an organic solvent (alcohol and/ or acetone) is applied for a few seconds. This solvent will wash the precipitate right out of a Gram-negative cell, but the color will remain in a Gram-positive cell if not left on too long. Lastly, a second stain called a counterstain must be applied. The counterstain has to be a different color than the first stain, and it will cause the colorless Gram negatives to pick up enough color to be visible in the microscope.

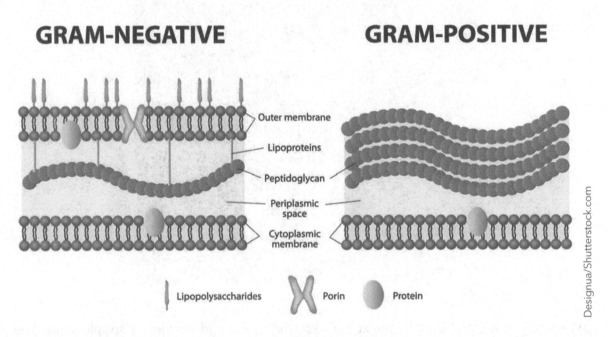

In the coming weeks, you will perform additional differential stains with similar steps. Here we want to learn the proper terminology used to describe these steps using the Gram stain as a model. The first colored stain applied during a differential stain is called the **primary stain**. In the case of the Gram stain, crystal violet is the primary stain. Usually, the second step is to use a mordant. A **mordant** will cause the primary stain to stick tighter to a specimen than it would by itself. An iodine solution called Gram's iodine is used in the Gram stain, and it reacts with crystal violet to form the insoluble precipitate with a dark purple color called a **CV-I complex** that sticks in the peptidoglycan. If the iodine step is not used, then the precipitate will not form and the stain will not turn out properly.

The third step is usually a **decolorization** step. During this step, a solvent is used that will wash the color out of some structures but not all of them. In the Gram stain, the alcohol decolorizer will wash the color out of Gram negatives but not Gram positives. The final step of a differential stain is usually a **counterstain** that must be a different color from the primary stain so it can stick to any colorless structures to make them visible and distinguishable from the structures colored by the primary stain. In the Gram stain, safranin is used as the counterstain and has a light reddish-pink color to it. The final result is that Gram positives will be purple from the primary stain and Gram negatives will be reddish-pink from the counterstain.

Exercise #1   Steps of the Gram Stain

Procedure – Solutions and Time of Application

Your instructor will use a colored diagram on the board to walk you through the steps of the Gram stain. Next, record the four basic steps of the Gram stain in the first table located in the results section, by indicating what solution to put on the slide and how long to leave it on the slide.

Another thing to start being aware of this week as we do this second stain is to start learning how to recognize the shapes and arrangements of bacterial cells. The two most common shapes of bacteria are the cocci (singular: coccus) and the rods or bacilli (singular: bacillus). The word coccus means berry shaped and they look like grapes or berries in the microscope showing up as almost perfect circles. Bacilli are rod shaped, which means they are longer in one dimension than they are wide so they are more cylindrical. The cocci are also more likely to make recognizable patterns or arrangements of cells that can help in their identification. The word **streptococcus** means that the cocci appear in long twisted chains that resemble a pearl necklace. Some of them appear in pairs that we call a **diplococcus**. **Staphylococcus** means that the cells form more of a random packet that looks like clusters of grapes. The following diagram shows the shapes and arrangements of bacterial cells as well as some others that are more rare.

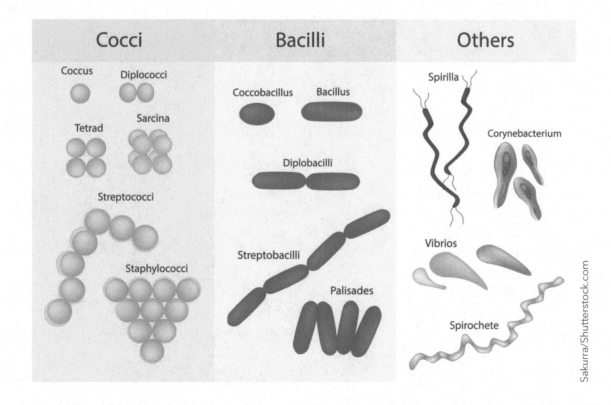

Sakurra/Shutterstock.com

DAY 1: RESULTS

Steps of the Gram Stain

Step	Compound	Duration
Primary stain		
Mordant		
Decolorizer		
Counterstain		

Briefly draw the results of your Gram stain and describe the shape, color, and arrangement of the bacteria on your slide

source: Roger Lightner

1. Which staining procedure only uses one color of stain?

   a. simple stain
   b. differential stain

2. The Gram stain is an example of a:

   a. simple stain
   b. differential stain

3. Which of the following has a cell wall consisting of a thin layer of peptidoglycan with an outer membrane?

   a. Gram positives
   b. Gram negatives

4. What is the primary stain for the Gram stain?

   a. safranin
   b. alcohol
   c. crystal violet
   d. iodine

5. Which of the following is the counterstain for the Gram stain?

   a. safranin
   b. alcohol
   c. crystal violet
   d. iodine

6. What does a mordant do?

   a. it decolorizes proteins
   b. it makes the primary stain stick tighter
   c. it reacts with the counterstain
   d. it keeps the smear from washing off of the slide

7. Which type of bacteria lose their color during the decolorization step with alcohol?

   a. Gram positive
   b. Gram negative

8. After performing the Gram stain, what color will Gram-positive bacteria be?

   a. purple
   b. pink/red
   c. green
   d. blue

9. Which bacterial shape looks like berries so they appear as circles in the microscope?
   a. cocci
   b. rods/bacilli

10. Which arrangement of bacterial cells looks like clusters of grapes?
   a. diplococcus
   b. streptococcus
   c. staphylococcus
   d. streptobacillus

4

Differential Stains: Endospore Stain and Environmental Effects on Growth

DAY 1: ENDOSPORES AND INOCULATIONS

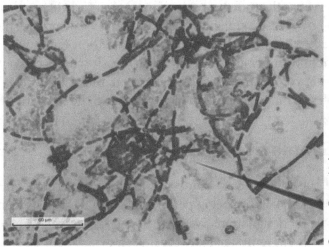

Source: Roger Lightner

Last week you learned your first differential stain, the Gram stain. This week we will learn another differential stain using similar steps to look for bacterial endospores. The word spore is used pretty loosely in biology, and many organisms produce spores. For instance, fungi produce spores as a reproductive mechanism similar to plants producing seeds. However, bacterial spores are not involved in reproduction and are produced inside the cell, so they should be more correctly called **endospores**. Not all bacteria produce endospores and the ones that do happen to all be Gram positive rods if you perform a Gram stain on them. The endospore is a survival mechanism that these bacteria produce to survive harsh conditions, such as high temperatures and low moisture. This is similar to a tree dropping its leaves and going dormant for the winter time. These bacteria will produce a dormant spore to ride out the harsh conditions and then when conditions become favorable again, the spore can germinate back into an active state called a **vegetative cell**. Since each vegetative cell produces only one endospore and that endospore germinates back into one cell, there is no multiplication and, therefore, it is not a reproductive mechanism.

Most endospore-forming organisms are harmless and very commonly found anywhere that is dusty or dirty. There are a few famous diseases caused by endospore-forming bacteria with Anthrax probably being the most famous one. There is a group of bacteria from the genus *Clostridium* that causes several diseases. *Clostridium perfringens* causes gangrene, *Clostridium tetani* causes tetanus,

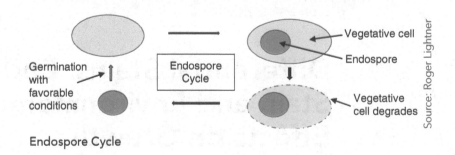

Endospore Cycle

and *Clostridium botulinum* causes botulism. A fourth species is called *Clostridiodes difficile* and is becoming more and more famous for causing antibiotic-associated colitis, a dangerous infection of the intestines associated with strong antibiotic usage. Many people have named it **Cdif**.

Endospores contain very thick protein coats that do not stain easily; so one way to visualize them is to perform a simple stain and look for the **window effect**. The simple stain will stain the vegetative cells, and the endospores will appear as blank windows inside the cell. There is an endospore staining procedure that will make the endospores more visible. The **primary stain** used is called **malachite green**. It is a blue-green colored stain that must be heated over the Bunsen burner to drive the stain into the endospore. The **heat** from this procedure serves as the **mordant** step. Your instructor will perform a demonstration on the heating procedure showing how to use a small piece of paper towel to keep the smear hot and moist during the 5-minute heating process. After heating, the slide is rinsed thoroughly with **water**; this serves as the **decolorization** step. It is not fully understood why the water washes the green out of everything except for the endospores. The last step is to **counterstain** with **safranin** to make the vegetative cells visible. When the staining procedure is completed, the endospores will be green and the vegetative cells will be reddish/pink.

Exercise #1   Simple Stain – Window Effect

Each lab table will have one culture of an endospore-forming bacterium. The unknown "Pet" cultures will also be distributed this week so you can begin performing tests to aid in its identification. The "Pet" bacterium will be labeled with a letter designation. Everyone in your group will want to record what letter of organism you will be working with this semester. Have the first student at your table prepare a microscope slide with two smears as shown in the following diagram and perform a simple stain to observe the window effect.

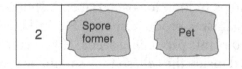

Procedure

- Prepare your specimen by taking a microscope slide and writing a number "2" on the frosted end to keep track of the top of the slide.
- Place two drops of water equally spaced on the slide.
- In the first drop, smear in some of the endospore-producing bacterium.
- In the second drop, smear in some of your "Pet" bacterium.
- Allow the smears to air dry or dry on the slide warmer and then heat fix over the Bunsen burner.
- Perform a simple stain with Crystal violet for 1 minute.
- Rinse the slide with water, blot dry, and observe with oil immersion to look for windows.

Exercise #2   Endospore Stain

Have a second student at the table prepare a smear of the two cultures in the similar manner as discussed earlier. This time the student will perform the steps of an endospore stain. This will allow students to see what endospores look like when stained and then determine whether your "Pet" is an endospore former.

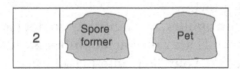

Procedure

- Prepare your specimen by taking a microscope slide and writing a number "2" on the frosted end to keep track of the top of the slide.
- Place two drops of water equally spaced on the slide.
- In the first drop, smear in some of the endospore-producing bacterium.
- In the second drop, smear in some of your "Pet" bacterium.
- Allow the smears to air dry or dry on the slide warmer and then heat fix over the Bunsen burner.
- Place a small piece of paper towel over the two smears on the slide and wet it down with malachite green.
- Using a clothespin, to keep from burning your fingertips, gently heat the slide over the Bunsen burner for 5 minutes keeping the stain moist and steaming hot.
- After 5 minutes, discard the paper towel piece with a pair of forceps and rinse the slide thoroughly with water.
- Flood both smears with safranin for 1 minute.
- Rinse the slide off and blot dry.
- Observe the slide under oil immersion to see what the spores look like and then determine whether your "Pet" is a spore former.

Exercise #3   Pet Gram Stain

Have all the other students at your table perform a Gram stain of the "Pet" bacterium. This will be good practice and start giving you valuable information for the identification of your unknown. When starting to identify a bacterium, the first thing you want to know is whether it is Gram positive or negative and what shapes and arrangements the cells make. Review the steps of the Gram stain from last week's lab.

Exercise #4   Environmental Factors That Affect Growth

There are four environmental factors that affect the growth of living organisms: **temperature, pH, osmotic pressure,** and **oxygen concentrations**. Temperature and pH affect the hydrogenbonds that hold proteins and nucleic acids together. Osmotic pressure refers to pressure placed on the membrane by osmosis because the solute concentrations on each side of the membrane are not equal. Some bacteria require oxygen like higher organisms do and others prefer to live without it.

Temperature: Bacteria that are adapted to grow best at temperatures below room temperature are called **psychrophiles**. Organisms that grow best from room temperature to a little above human body temperature are called **mesophiles**. Bacteria that grow best above 50°C are referred to as **thermophiles**. We will expose your "Pet" bacterium to four different temperatures and record how well it grows next week. Inoculate four Tryptic Soy Broth (TSB) tubes with your "Pet" and label them with the four temperatures, according to the growth table in the results section. Next week you will record how heavy the turbidity of the broth is using a – sign for no growth, + for a little growth, ++ for moderate growth, and +++ for heavy growth.

pH: Most bacteria will be **neutrophiles**, meaning they do not like the pH too far away from neutral pH. Bacteria that thrive at low pH are called **acidophiles**. Bacteria that grow best at high pH are referred to as **alkaliphiles**. Inoculate your "Pet" into pH adjusted TSB tubes that are shown in the table in the results section and record the growth results next week.

When the solute concentration is higher outside the cell than inside, it results in a **hypertonic** situation. Cells are in danger of dehydrating and shriveling under hypertonic conditions. Inoculate your "Pet" onto salt adjusted Tryptic Soy Agar (TSA) agar plates according to the concentrations in the table in the results section and record the growth results. **Halotolerant** bacteria are capable of growing in up to 10% or 20% NaCl. True **halophiles** require very high salt concentrations such as we see at the Great Salt Lake in Utah.

Most of us deal with higher organisms such as animals that require oxygen for growth and metabolism. However, in the microbial world, we actually see organisms that can survive without oxygen and some that actually die if they come in contact with it. **Aerobes** or **obligate aerobes** are bacteria that require oxygen just like you do and they only carry out cellular respiration. **Anaerobes** live without oxygen and can be more specifically subdivided into obligate anaerobes and aerotolerant anaerobes. **Obligate anaerobes** must be in anaerobic environments and die if they are exposed to oxygen. The most famous group of bacteria that fit this description is the **Clostridia** that were mentioned earlier as being endospore formers. **Aerotolerant anaerobes** can survive in the presence of oxygen, but they do not use it. They only carry out fermentation, even if the oxygen is present, so they are sometimes called **obligate fermenters**. The most famous obligate fermenters are the **Streptococci**. **Facultative anaerobes** are versatile and can live with or without oxygen. If oxygen is present, they will carry out cellular respiration; if it is absent, they can switch over to fermentation and still grow even if it is at a slower rate. Many famous bacteria such as *Escherichia coli* are facultative anaerobes.

One medium that is commonly used to determine the oxygen conditions a bacterium prefers is called **Thioglycolate broth**. Thioglycolate is a compound that keeps oxygen from dissolving completely to the bottom of the test tube. A color reagent that turns pink in the presence of oxygen is added to the medium to visually detect where the oxygen is located. An uninoculated Thioglycolate tube should have a pink ring at the top showing that there is a small aerobic zone, but the rest of the tube has a tan color indicating that the bottom of the tube is anaerobic. Inoculate a tube of Thioglycolate broth with your "Pet" and incubate it until next week. Determine whether your "Pet" is an aerobe, anaerobe, or facultative anaerobe based on the location of the growth. Aerobes will grow at the top, anaerobes at the bottom, and facultative anaerobes will be able to grow all the way through the entire tube. In the table in the results section, record + for growth and – for no growth in the zones of the tube to help you identify the type of bacteria you have.

Pet ID: At the front of the lab manual on page xi is a Pet Identification form that you can start filling out. It will take about three weeks to complete the form, but you can start with the information you learned today. From your Gram stain, you should know whether it is Gram positive or negative and whether it is a coccus or a rod. You can also note if you see any special arrangements of cells such as clusters or chains. In addition, you should know if it is an endospore producer. Record the information you learn about your pet from this lab on the Pet ID form.

DAY 1: RESULTS

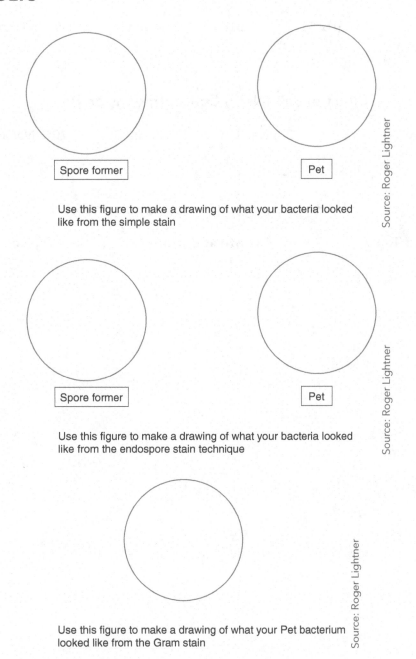

Spore former

Pet

Use this figure to make a drawing of what your bacteria looked like from the simple stain

Source: Roger Lightner

Spore former

Pet

Use this figure to make a drawing of what your bacteria looked like from the endospore stain technique

Source: Roger Lightner

Use this figure to make a drawing of what your Pet bacterium looked like from the Gram stain

Source: Roger Lightner

DAY 2: RESULTS

Last week you inoculated several plates and tubes to test the effects of environmental factors of your "Pet" bacterium. Go back and fill in the tables to indicate which conditions your bacterium was able to grow in and not able to grow in. Describe what type of bacterium you have for each of the four environmental factors on the Pet Identification Form you started filling in last week

Effect of Temperature on Pet

4°C	23°C	37°C	60°C	Type of Organism

Effect of pH on Pet

pH 3	pH 5	pH 7	pH 9	Type of Organism

Effect of Salt (NaCl) Concentrations on Pet

Control	5% NaCl	10% NaCl	20% NaCl

Effects of Oxygen Concentration on Pet

Growth at Top	Growth at Bottom	Type of Organism

1. What is the primary stain for the endospore stain?

    a. crystal violet
    b. malachite green
    c. methylene blue
    d. safranin

2. If you do a simple stain or Gram stain on a culture that has endospores, then the spores will appear:

    a. green
    b. red/pink
    c. as Windows
    d. blue

3. What is the mordant for the endospore stain?

    a. iodine
    b. water
    c. heat
    d. alcohol

4. What is the decolorizer for the endospore stain?

    a. iodine
    b. water
    c. heat
    d. alcohol

5. After performing the endospore stain, any spores should be:

    a. green
    b. red/pink
    c. blue
    d. yellow

6. After performing the endospore stain, the vegetative cells should be:

    a. green
    b. red/pink
    c. blue
    d. yellow

7. Bacterial endospores are produced as a:

    a. survival mechanism
    b. means of reproduction

8. Which of the following bacterial groups are famous spore producers and disease causers?

    a. Streptococci
    b. Staphylococci
    c. Gram-negative rods
    d. Clostridia

9. If your Pet bacteria only grows at the top of a Fluid Thioglycolate tube, then you would classify it as a(n):

    a. aerobe
    b. anaerobe
    c. facultative anaerobe

10. Which of the following bacterial groups are famous for being halotolerant and growing at salt concentrations as high as 20%?

    a. Streptococci
    b. Staphylococci
    c. Gram-negative rods
    d. Clostridia

LAB WEEK

5

Capsule Stain (Negative Staining), Acid-Fast Stain, and Selective Media

DAY 1: STAINING AND INOCULATIONS

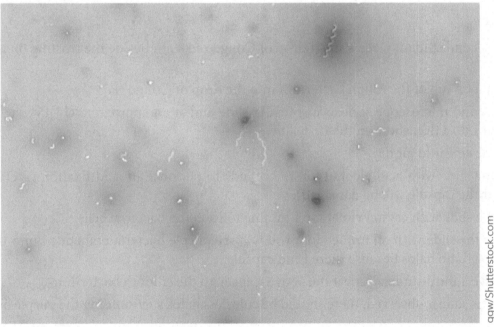

ggw/Shutterstock.com

This week we will learn about additional stains, including the capsule stain and acid-fast staining technique. The capsule stain utilizes what is called a negative stain. So far, everything we have done have been **positive stains** where the stain sticks to the bacterial cell, making it darker. With a **negative stain**, the background is stained and the bacterial cell remains colorless. One student will perform a negative stain with **Nigrosine** on your "Pet" bacterium. You may be pleasantly surprised to see that you can distinguish shapes and arrangements of cells better with this stain than you could with the Gram stain.

Capsules are structures that some bacteria have that coat the outside of the cell and camouflage the protein surface structures from the human immune system. This can make the bacterium potentially pathogenic. Capsules are made of polysaccharide, which the immune system does not recognize as readily and does not stain as easily as proteins do. The capsule stain will use a negative stain called Congo red to stain the background. Next, this will be followed up with a positive stain using crystal violet to stain the bacterial cells purple. The capsule actually does not stain so it appears as a colorless halo around the outside of the cell.

Exercise #1   Negative Stain

Procedure

- Have one student at your table place a small drop of Nigrosine stain beside the frosting on a microscope slide.
- Smear a loop full of your "Pet" bacterium right into the Nigrosine stain.
- Use a second microscope slide as a spreader slide and at an approximately 45° angle spread the stain out into a thin sheet on the first slide.
- Allow the smear to air dry.
- View the slide with oil immersion to observe colorless cells embedded into a darker background.

Exercise #2   Capsule Stain

Procedure

- Have a second student place a small drop of Congo red stain beside the frosting on a microscope slide.
- Smear a loop full of the rough bacterium into the drop of Congo red.
- Use a second microscope slide as a spreader slide and at an approximately 45° angle spread the stain out into a thin sheet on the first slide.
- Allow the smear to air dry.
- Flood the slide with acid alcohol for 15 seconds to perform an acid fixation (DO NOT HEAT FIX!!! or the capsule will be damaged).
- Flood the slide with crystal violet for 1 minute to stain the bacterial cells.
- Observe the slide with oil immersion; you will see purple bacteria embedded into the red background with no halos because there is no capsule.
- Now, have a third student repeat the above steps with the smooth bacterium.
- When this slide is observed, there should be colorless halos surrounding the purple bacterial cells.

Acid-Fast Stain

The last stain we will discuss is the Acid-Fast Stain. This stain has traditionally been used to identify the tuberculosis bacterium. Tuberculosis or TB is caused by an unusual bacterium called *Mycobacterium tuberculosis*. **Mycobacteria** are unique because they contain a very waxy substance called **mycolic acid** in their cell wall. Mycolic acid does not stain well so this bacterium is difficult to Gram stain. This staining procedure utilizes a **primary stain** called Carbol Fuchsin, which is a reddish-purple colored stain. It has to be heated over the Bunsen burner to drive it into the mycolic acid. The **heat** is the **mordant** for the stain. The third step is to **decolorize** with **acid alcohol**. This strong decolorizer will wash the Carbol Fuchsin out of everything, except a *Mycobacterium*. **Methylene Blue** is used as a **counterstain** to stain all other types of bacteria. Mycobacteria will be reddish-purple while other types are blue. Mycobacteria are said to be **acid-fast** because even after the acid wash, they hold fast to the Carbol Fuchsin while other bacteria do not. Have one student at your table perform the following acid-fast stain procedure on both your "Pet" and a culture of *Mycobacterium smegmatis*.

Exercise #3   Acid-Fast Stain

Procedure

- Make a slide with two smears on it. Smear the *Mycobacterium smegmatis* in a drop of water on the left and your "Pet" in a drop on the right.
- Allow these smears to air dry or dry on the slide warmer.
- Heat fix the slide in the Bunsen burner.
- Flood the slide with carbolfuchsin and heat the slide gently for five minutes over the Bunsen burner.
- Rinse the slide with water
- Decolorize the slide by holding it at an angle over a sink and rinsing it with acid-alcohol until no more color is coming off the slide.
- Counterstain the slide with methylene blue for one minute at room temperature.
- Rinse the slide with water and blot dry with bibulous paper.
- View the slide with oil immersion and compare/contrast the two cultures.

Selective Media

Our next topic is selective and differential media. **Selective media** contain chemicals that inhibit the growth of unwanted organisms while allowing a target group to grow because they are resistant to chemical additive. Most selective media select for either Gram-positive bacteria or Gram-negative bacteria. You will inoculate a Tryptic Soy Agar (TSA) plate to show that it is a nonselective medium.

Mannitol Salt Agar (MSA) is a good introductory medium for these concepts because it is both selective and differential. **Differential media** contain color reagents that change color to indicate that a specific chemical reaction has occurred. The most common reagents used are pH indicators. MSA contains a high enough salt concentration that it inhibits most bacteria, but **Staphylococci** can still grow because they are **halotolerant**. There is also a pH indicator called **phenol red** added to indicate if the carbohydrate mannitol is fermented or not. Fermentation usually yields acid products that lower the pH, and phenol red turns yellow to indicate that this has happened. There are two species of *Staphylococcus*. *Staphylococcus epidermidis* is a relatively harmless species that we all have on our skin. It does not ferment mannitol so it feeds on protein in the medium. Protein metabolism usually yields ammonia, which is a base, so it causes the pH to go up where phenol red turns fuchsia. *Staphylococcus aureus* is a famous pathogen that does ferment mannitol, causing the medium to turn yellow. These two drastically different color changes easily allow for the differentiation of the two species.

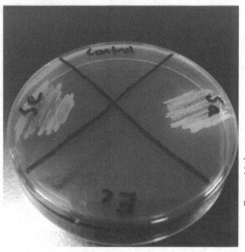

source: Roger Lightner

Eosin Methylene Blue (EMB) Agar is a medium that selects for Gram-negative bacteria. Stains or dies like Eosin and Methylene Blue usually kill Gram-positive bacteria, but Gram negatives are resistant to them. When working with Gram-negative rod-shaped bacteria, we usually want to know if they are lactose fermenters or not. EMB has lactose in it along with a pH indicator. When the bacterium ferments the lactose and releases acid, the medium turns a dark purple color. Nonfermenters produce a colorless growth. *Escherichia coli* is probably the most famous **lactose fermenter** so it produces a very dark color seen from the bottom of the plate and on the top a very unique **green sheen** that makes it easy to identify.

MacConkey (MAC) Agar is very similar to EMB but is even more selective. It contains Crystal violet to kill off Gram positives and bile salts to kill off bacteria that do not live in the intestinal tract. This makes MAC selective for Gram-negative **enteric** bacteria. It also has lactose sugar along with a pH indicator. Lactose fermenters will produce a pink color, with the color being brighter and stronger according to the amount of fermentation taking place. Nonfermenters also produce a colorless growth on this medium.

source: Roger Lightner

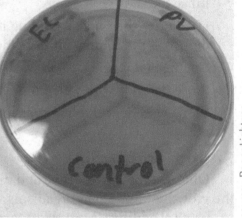
source: Roger Lightner

Exercise #4   Differential and Selective Agar Plates

Procedure

- Using your "Pet" bacterium as an inoculum, perform an isolation streak plate procedure on a TSA plate. This will allow you to see that TSA is nonselective and also give you colonies to describe that may help with identification.
- Inoculate a MSA plate with just a zig-zag streak down the middle of it with your "Pet."
- Inoculate an EMB plate with just a zig-zag streak down the middle of it with your "Pet."
- Inoculate a MAC plate with just a zig-zag streak down the middle of it with your "Pet."
- You just need one set of these plates per lab table.

DAY 1: RESULTS

Use this figure to make a drawing of what your pet bacterium looked like from the nigrosine negative stain

source: Roger Lightner

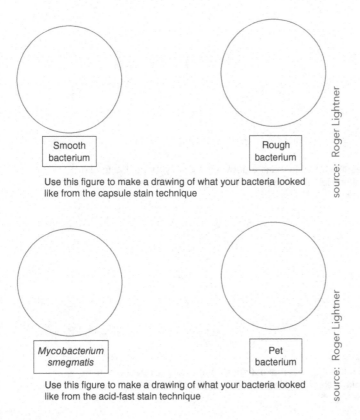

Smooth
bacterium

Rough
bacterium

Use this figure to make a drawing of what your bacteria looked
like from the capsule stain technique

source: Roger Lightner

*Mycobacterium
smegmatis*

Pet
bacterium

Use this figure to make a drawing of what your bacteria looked
like from the acid-fast stain technique

source: Roger Lightner

DAY 2: RESULTS

Last week you were introduced to the concept of selective and differential media. You will take the first few minutes of lab this week to record the growth results of your "Pet" bacterium on the four agar plates you streaked. Following your instructor's lead, record how your "Pet" grew on the Tryptic Soy Agar (TSA), Mannitol Salt Agar (MSA), Eosin Methylene Blue (EMB) Agar, and MacConkey Agar plates on your **"Pet" Identification Form** on **page xi**.

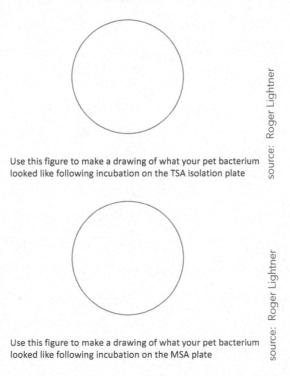

Use this figure to make a drawing of what your pet bacterium
looked like following incubation on the TSA isolation plate

source: Roger Lightner

Use this figure to make a drawing of what your pet bacterium
looked like following incubation on the MSA plate

source: Roger Lightner

Use this figure to make a drawing of what your pet bacterium looked like following incubation on the EMB plate

source: Roger Lightner

Use this figure to make a drawing of what your pet bacterium looked like following incubation on the MAC plate

source: Roger Lightner

1. What does a negative stain stick to?

    a. bacterial cell
    b. background

2. What is the primary or negative stain used in the capsule stain?

    a. crystal violet
    b. safranin
    c. malachite green
    d. Congo red

3. After performing the capsule stain, how do the capsules appear?

    a. red
    b. colorless halos
    c. purple
    d. blue

4. What type of bacterium is the Acid-Fast Stain used to detect?

    a. Gram positive
    b. Gram negative
    c. Mycobacteria
    d. Cyanobacteria

5. What famous disease is caused by an acid-fast bacterium?

    a. strep throat
    b. tetanus
    c. tuberculosis
    d. syphilis

6. Which type of medium contains chemicals that change color to indicate a particular reaction has taken place?

    a. complex medium
    b. selective medium
    c. differential medium
    d. enrichment medium

7. Which bacterium causes MSA to turn yellow?

    a. *S. aureus*
    b. *S. epidermidis*
    c. *Enterococcus faecalis*
    d. *E. coli*

8. Which bacterium is famous for producing a "green sheen" on EMB Agar?

    a. *S. aureus*
    b. *S. epidermidis*
    c. *E. faecalis*
    d. *E. coli*

9. What type of bacteria does EMB Agar select for?
   a. Gram positives
   b. Gram negatives
   c. Mycobacteria
   d. Cyanobacteria

10. What color will a lactose fermenter produce on MAC Agar?
   a. yellow
   b. purple/black
   c. pink
   d. white

6

Biochemical Tests: Differential Media and EnteroPluri Test

DAY 1: INOCULATIONS OF DIFFERENTIAL MEDIA

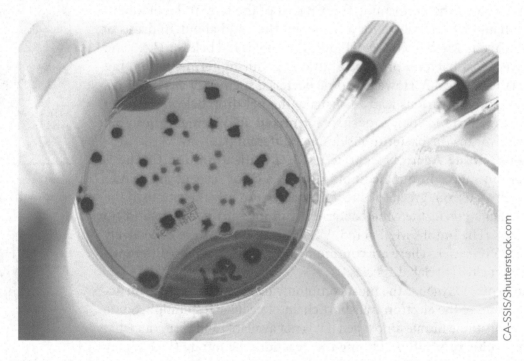

CA-SSIS/Shutterstock.com

This week you will inoculate your "Pet" into a variety of differential test media. The following will give a brief description of each medium used and how the results will be read next week. You will again see that these results will be added to your "Pet" Identification Form after they are read next week. After that you should have enough information to key out and identify your unknown bacterium. In the front of the lab manual on pages xii and xiii, there are a **dichotomous key** and flowchart to aid you in your identification.

Source: Roger Lightner

Phenol Red Broth: Phenol red broth is used to identify which carbohydrates a bacterial species is capable of fermenting. Phenol red is a commonly used pH indicator in microbiology labs. It is **red** at **neutral** pH but turns **yellow** under **acidic** conditions and **fuchsia** under **alkaline** conditions. Since acid products are common from the fermentation of carbohydrates, a color change from red to yellow is a positive test result for fermentation. These tubes will also have an upside down fermentation vial or **Durham tube** inside that will capture a gas bubble if any gaseous molecules are produced. Gas production or the lack thereof can also be indicative of certain species of bacteria. Results are recorded in shorthand with a letter "**A**" used for a yellow color that indicates **acid** and a letter "**G**" used to indicate any **gas** production. If the medium remains red or turns fuchsia and there is no gas bubble, the result is recorded as (−/−), which means negative for both acid and gas. If the tube turns yellow with no gas bubble, then the result is recorded as (A/−) indicating the bacterium is positive for acid production but negative for gas. Lastly, if the tube turns yellow and there

is a gas bubble present, then the results are recorded as (A/G) showing that the organism is positive for both acid and gas production. You will be inoculating four Phenol red broth tubes containing **glucose, lactose, mannitol,** and **glycerol** as the carbohydrates present.

Tryptone Broth: Tryptone broth contains the amino acid tryptophan. Some bacteria can break down tryptophan to produce a compound called **indole**. After the bacteria have grown in the broth, you add about five drops of a solution called **Kovac's reagent,** and if a **red ring** develops at the top of the tube, this is a positive indication of indole production.

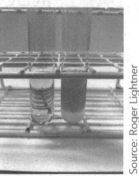

MRVP Broth: MRVP is an acronym for **methyl red Voges-Proskauer** medium. We will not be performing the VP part of the test. You will inoculate the broth and let it incubate for a week and then add about 10 drops of methyl red reagent. Methyl red is a pH indicator that is red below pH 4.3 and yellow above. Most bacteria produce a little acid during fermentation, but the pH remains above 4.3. However, some bacteria, such as *Escherichia coli*, produce a mixture of various acids that make the pH drop below 4.3. After adding the reagent, a red color is positive for **mixed acid fermentation,** but a yellow color means the bacterium is doing a different pathway.

Simmons Citrate Agar: The citrate test is a **utilization** test. Citrate is the only carbon source in the medium. There is a color reagent in the medium that will turn from green to blue if the bacterium eats the citrate. If the medium remains green, then the bacterium cannot eat the citrate and no growth occurs. The Indole, Methyl red, VP, and Citrate tests are collectively called the **IMViC** series. These are commonly used tests that help differentiate *E. coli* from closely related species.

Nitrate Broth: Oxygen is the most commonly used **terminal electron acceptor** at the end of the electron transport chain of cellular respiration. Some bacteria can substitute nitrate for oxygen if it is not available and carry out what is called **anaerobic respiration**. During this reaction, the nitrate (NO_3^-) may be converted to nitrite (NO_2^-) or be broken down even further to nitrogen gas (N_2). This broth is inoculated and allowed to incubate. There is a Durham tube added; so if there is a gas bubble present, this is a positive reaction because the NO_3^- was converted to N_2. If there is no gas bubble, you will add 10 drops each of 2 reagents called nitrate reagents A and B. After the reagents are added, they will turn red if the NO_3^- was converted to NO_2^- and this is a positive test. If no color change takes place, then the nitrate is still there and no reaction took place. An additional confirmation is that if a small pinch of zinc powder is added to the tube, it will cause the nitrate to turn red, thus proving that the bacteria did not utilize it.

Source: Roger Lightner

Source: Roger Lightner

Source: Roger Lightner

Source: Roger Lightner

Starch Hydrolysis: The starch hydrolysis test is performed on a starch agar plate. This medium looks just like TSA so it is important to have it labeled. Some bacteria produce the *amylase* enzyme that humans produce in their saliva. If a bacterium produces *amylase,* the starch will be eaten out of the medium. The starch is dissolved in the agar and is invisible to the naked eye. In order to visualize the starch, a couple of droppers full of the Gram's iodine solution flooded on the plate will make it visible. Starch reacts with iodine to form a dark blue to purple color. You will make a single streak of your "Pet" down the middle of the plate and let it incubate. Next week you will add the iodine to see where the starch is. If the blue /purple color surrounds the bacterium, then it is negative for *amylase*. If you observe a clear zone around the bacterium, then it is positive because the *amylase* ate the starch and there is nothing there for the iodine to react with.

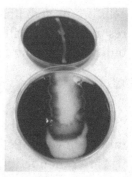

Triple Sugar Iron (TSI) Agar: TSI agar is in a slanted tube. It will start with a red color because it contains phenol red pH indicator. This is a good medium for indicating aerobes and facultative anaerobes. Aerobes will not ferment the sugars so the tube will remain red or maybe fuchsia at the top. Facultative anaerobes carry out respiration at the top and fermentation at the bottom so you may get a fuchsia slant with the butt of the tube being yellow. Strong fermenters will turn the entire tube yellow. If there is any gas produced, there will be lifting, cracking, and splitting of the agar. In addition, there is iron added to the medium, which will react with any hydrogen sulfide gas (H_2S) to produce a black color. Hydrogen sulfide production is produced by a small number of bacteria anaerobically, with *Salmonella* being the most famous. The black color is usually primarily at the bottom of the tube, and we use *Proteus* bacteria as a safer alternative to working with *Salmonella*.

Gelatin Liquefaction: Robert Koch had a problem with bacteria-eating gelatin he was trying to use as a solidifying agent before he was told about agar. Not all bacteria eat gelatin so it can be used as a diagnostic tool. Gelatin deep tubes are made by adding 12% gelatin to Tryptic Soy Broth (TSB) and allowing them to harden straight up. They are usually inoculated with a needle by stabbing straight down into the medium. After the tubes incubate for a week, if the tube is still solid, it is negative; but if it has turned at least partially to liquid, then it is positive, which means the bacterium is eating away the gelatin.

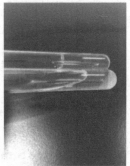

Bile Esculin Agar: Some bacteria, especially members of the Streptococci, are capable of hydrolyzing a compound called esculin. This medium will be an agar slant that is inoculated with a needle. If the bacterium is positive for this reaction, the medium will turn black. Staphylococci do not carry out this reaction so it can be helpful in differentiating these two groups of Gram-positive cocci.

Motility Test Medium: Most bacteria that are motile use flagella to swim. Some bacteria are not motile, especially Gram-positive cocci. Motility medium contains a soft agar that bacteria can swim through. The tube is inoculated by stabbing the bacteria straight down with a needle. This traps bacterial

Source: Roger Lightner
Source: Roger Lightner
Source: Roger Lightner
Source: Roger Lightner
Source: Roger Lightner

cells on the stab line. If the bacterium is negative for motility, it can only grow on the stab line and the rest of the tube will be clear. If the bacterium has flagella, it will swim away from the stab line and turbidity will be seen fanning out through the tube.

Exercise #1   Inoculation of Differential Media

The previous paragraphs give a general overview of how each medium works. This week you will inoculate your "Pet" bacterium into each medium, and next week we will look at the results of each test after incubation. In general, we will record both positive and negative test results. Usually, a positive test means that a color change or reaction took place. A negative test means that no reaction took place and probably no color change occurred. The following procedure lists will help you make sure that you inoculate all the media provided. Your instructor will demonstrate inoculation tips but in general if you are inoculating a broth, you only have to touch the broth with a loop-full of your "Pet" using aseptic technique. If there is an agar deep, you will use the inoculating needle to stab straight down the middle of the tube. If there is an agar slant, you want to stab through the agar to the bottom of the tube and then fishtail streak the slant. Place all the inoculated tubes and plates where the instructor designates for incubation.

Procedure

- You will inoculate one set of biochemical tests for your "Pet" per table or lab group. Decide among yourselves how the work will be divided up and make sure to label all media.
- Obtain one of each of the four **Phenol red broths** containing **glucose**, **lactose**, **mannitol,** and **glycerol**. Inoculate using aseptic technique and flame the loop between tubes to prevent chemical contamination.
- Obtain one **Tryptone broth** tube and inoculate it.
- Obtain one **MRVP broth** tube and inoculate it.
- Obtain one **Simmons citrate agar slant** and inoculate it with a stab and streak method.
- Obtain one **nitrate broth** and inoculate it.
- Obtain one **starch agar plate** and inoculate it with a single streak down the middle.
- Obtain one **TSI agar slant** and inoculate it with the stab and streak method.
- Obtain one **Gelatin deep** tube and inoculate it with a stab down the middle.
- Obtain one **Bile Esculin agar slant** and inoculate it with a stab and streak method.
- Obtain one **Motility test medium** and inoculate it with a stab straight down the middle.

Exercise #2   EnteroPluri Test

Now that you have learned about several biochemical tests that can be performed individually, the next thing to introduce you to is a rapid test. The EnteroPluri test is a well-known one that is used to identify bacteria that are members of the family Enterobacteriaceae. This means they are in the same family as *E. coli* and are intestinal organisms. The first criterion to use the EnteroPluri test is that the bacteria must all be Gram-negative rods that are oxidase negative. **Oxidase** positive bacteria are aerobes that have an enzyme called oxidase as part of their electron transport chain. Facultative anaerobes will not have this enzyme and test negative. To perform the oxidase test, you will drop a little oxidase reagent from a provided dropper on top of the agar plate containing your "Pet" bacterium.

If the bacteria turn blue within about 3 minutes, it is oxidase positive and no color change is negative. Separate cultures will be provided to inoculate the EnteroPluri test because not all of the "Pets" are in this family.

Procedure

- Obtain one EnteroPluri test per table and label it with the culture number you will be inoculating it with provided on your table. You will notice the test device is about the size of a large pen.
- Unscrew the white cap off of the tube and dip the needle into the culture to get bacteria on it.
- Unscrew the blue cap, grab the loop end of the metal rod, and pull it slowly through the tube. Observe to make sure that the tip of the needle touches all of the media wells to inoculate them and then push the rod back through the tube to plug the shaft back up. When the tip of the rod is at the end of the glucose test, there should be a notch in the shaft lined up with the other end. Bend the rod to break off the loop end.
- Screw the white and blue caps back on to the ends of the tube to keep contaminants out.
- Use the small piece of broken rod with the loop end to punch holes in the EnteroPluri tube. The tube is covered with cellophane and on the clear side of the tube you will see eight little windows to punch. This allows air into the tube for these aerobic tests. The other test wells do not have windows and are not punched because they will stay anaerobic.
- Give your inoculated tube to the instructor for incubation. Next week the materials for reading the tube will be provided online and your instructor will walk you through each step.

DAY 2: RESULTS

Use this page to make drawings of each differential test. Show the results that you got for your pet after incubation. Remember to also record each one on the Pet ID form on page xi. For the Enteropluri test you can fill in an example report form found in the the front of the manual on page xiv.

1. What color does phenol red turn under acidic conditions?

   a. yellow
   b. red
   c. fuchsia
   d. blue

2. Which sugar is more difficult to ferment?

   a. glucose/dextrose
   b. lactose

3. What is a positive test result in a tryptone broth tube?

   a. a red ring
   b. a yellow ring
   c. a black precipitate
   d. a gas bubble

4. A positive methyl red test means that the bacterium is carrying out which fermentation pathway?

   a. homolactic acid
   b. alcoholic
   c. mixed acid

5. What color reagent do you add to perform the starch hydrolysis test?

   a. Kovac's reagent
   b. Methyl red
   c. Gram's iodine

6. If you add reagents A and B to a nitrate tube and it turns red, what does this mean?

   a. the nitrate is still there and no reaction took place
   b. the nitrate has been converted to nitrite which is a positive test
   c. the nitrate has been converted to nitrogen gas which is considered positive

7. After incubation of a gelatin deep, what will a positive test result be?

   a. it has turned to liquid
   b. it has remained hardened

8. In TSI agar, what is a positive reaction for H_2S production?

   a. it turns yellow
   b. it turns black
   c. it turns fuchsia

9. What is a positive reaction for the Simmons citrate agar slant?

   a. blue
   b. yellow
   c. green
   d. fuchsia

10. If the bacterium only grows on the stab line of a motility test medium, then this means it is
    _____ for motility.

    a. positive
    b. negative

7

Serial Dilutions, and Plate Counting

DAY 1: DILUTIONS AND PLATE INOCULATIONS

sruilk/Shutterstock.com

As you may imagine, the counting or enumeration of microorganisms can be a little tricky because they are not visible to the naked eye. Counting microbes is not as easy as counting larger organisms. There is what is called a direct count where a technician would count the cells in the microscope using a special slide where the exact volume of sample is known. However, the direct count is quite tedious and is probably mostly used to count and identify algae. The enumeration of bacteria is usually completed by applying more indirect methods. The most widely used method of counting bacteria is probably the **serial dilution and standard plate count technique**. Most microbiologists will employ this at some time in their activities and usually call it **plate counting** for short. This technique can be used to test a wide variety of samples. We could test liquid samples such as water, milk, and juice or we could test solid samples such as soil or meat. This method is mainly used in the food and beverage industry or testing water quality. It can be important to know the concentration of microbes in food and beverages to ensure that the food we eat and the beverages we drink are safe to consume. Also, since bacteria are so small, their numbers are usually reported as concentration values such as cells per milliliter or 100 ml.

The first step is to perform dilutions in a series to cover a wide range of dilutions. This is particularly important for testing a sample that you have no history on and have no idea how much contamination may be present. If you were to put a little of the sample on an agar plate, it might be completely covered with growth, and you would only know that there is a lot there but not have a good number to work with. By diluting the sample over a wide range, you hope to get a dilution that you can use to back calculate to figure out what was in the original sample. Dilutions can be made in a variety of ways, but in plate counting we often work in factors of 10 so the calculation is easily made by just moving the decimal point.

Today we will employ two dilutions. The first and most common dilution you see is a **10-fold dilution**. This is achieved by pipetting 1 ml into a test tube containing 9 ml of a sterile water or buffered water. These sterile tubes are called **dilution blanks** because the fluid inside them is sterile and dilutes the sample without contributing any bacterial cells to the numbers. The amount of a dilution is calculated by taking the amount pipetted to the blank divided by the total volume after it is added. In this case, 1 ml is pipetted into a tube containing 9 ml so the final volume is 10 ml. This constitutes a 1/10 dilution or a 10-fold dilution. The second dilution is used when you have concentrated samples and want to dilute it down more quickly. We can achieve a **100-fold dilution** by pipetting 1 ml of sample into a larger bottle containing 99 ml of sterile water. When you do multiple dilutions that are linked together, this is a series that dilutes your sample in a stepwise manner and we can take subsamples from each tube or bottle. Your instructor will use an online diagram to walk you through a simple dilution series and show you how to calculate each dilution factor. **Dilution factors** show how much each dilution in the series is in comparison to the original sample. For example, if you pipette 1 ml of sample into a 9-ml dilution blank, then the first dilution factor is 10^{-1}. We usually write the dilution factor as an exponent rather than a fraction and 1/10 is equal to 10^{-1}. Now if I mix this first dilution tube up and pipette 1 ml of it into another 9 ml dilution blank, then I dilute my sample by another factor of 10. Since $10^{-1} \times 10^{-1} = 10^{-2}$, the second dilution tube has a dilution factor of 10^{-2}, showing that it is 100 times more dilute than the original sample.

Once the dilution series is completed, you are now ready to pipette a specific volume onto an agar plate. Since we keep track of the bacterial concentration as per ml, if we pipetted 1 ml onto the plate, it would not change our calculation any. However, 1 ml is really too much volume for performing a spread plate where the water is spread evenly on top of the agar, so smaller volumes, such as 0.1 ml or 0.2 ml, are often employed. This means that the dilution factor on the plate will be different from the tube it was pipetted from. If only 0.1 ml is pipetted to the plate, then you would only get 1/10 of the bacterial colonies that you would get if you pipetted a full ml. To account for this, you change your dilution factor by another factor of 10 so the decimal point will be moved an additional place. For example, if I pipette 0.1 ml from a dilution blank that has a dilution factor of 10^{-3}, then I would make the dilution factor on the plate 10^{-4}. Technically, the sample is not diluted, but the number of colonies are still be reduced by a factor of 10. Again, your instructor will demonstrate this on the hypothetical example provided online. One key concept to see here is that if you pipette 1 ml to a plate, it will not change your dilution factor, but pipetting 0.1 ml will change it by an additional factor of 10.

Next, we should discuss the difference between spread plates and pour plates. All labs will perform the **spread plate** method where the dilution water is pipetted onto the top of an agar plate where the agar is already in the plate. This creates a small puddle of water that is then spread evenly over the plate with a tool called a **cell spreader**. The cell spreader will have a flat surface that is dipped in alcohol and burned off to sterilize it before touching the plate, so no additional bacteria will be added to the sample. Any place a cell lands, it will grow into a colony during incubation and can then be counted to tell us how many bacterial cells were placed onto the plate. It is possible two or more cells could land so close together that they grow into one colony, so many textbooks record colony-forming units (cfus) rather than cells. Since all volumes pipetted and the number of dilutions made are kept track of, you can now use the colony count to back calculate the concentration of bacteria in the original sample. A second method that is sometimes used is called a **pour plate**. With this technique, you may pipette a full ml into a molten agar and then pour this agar into an empty Petri dish. You can swirl the plate to mix the contents. The molten agar is kept just hot enough so that it does not solidify but not hot enough to kill the bacteria. Once the agar is poured, it will harden quickly and the bacterial cells will be dispersed and trapped into the agar and then grow into colonies during incubation.

Exercise #1   Spread Plate Method

The diagram at the bottom of this page shows a schematic of the dilution series we will perform today using a bacterial culture tube as the original sample. The instructor will walk through the schematic on the board to help you calculate out what the dilution factors will be for each bottle and tube. The instructor will also perform a demonstration to show you how to use the instruments consisting of micropipetters and a **vortex** machine. Next week you will count the colonies and back calculate to see what the bacterial concentration was in the original tube.

In order to perform the back calculation, you take the number of colonies and multiply it by the dilution factor on the plate. You also want to drop the negative sign off of the exponent since you are going back the opposite direction. First, you need to determine which plate is the countable plate. A **countable plate** will have between **30 and 300 colonies** on it. Any plate with over 300 colonies will be too crowded or smeared to get a good count and we declare it **Too Numerous To Count (TNTC)**. If a plate has less than 30 colonies on it, then it is discarded for being statistically insignificant. For example, if I have a plate that has 237 colonies on it and the dilution factor is 10^{-5}, then the calculation would be as follows. The 237 colonies is in the range of 30 to 300 so it is countable. Next, I multiply it by the dilution factor dropping the negative sign which gives me 237×10^5. This is not correct scientific notation so I would report 2.37×10^7 cfus/ml as my final concentration. If you struggle with scientific notation, take the 237 colonies and put five zeros after it giving you 23700000. Next, move the decimal place between the 2 and 3 and then put in the proper exponent of 10^7. This would tell me that the original culture tube had a bacterial concentration of approximately 23,700,000 cells/ml. If you happen to have more than one countable plate, then you would average them together.

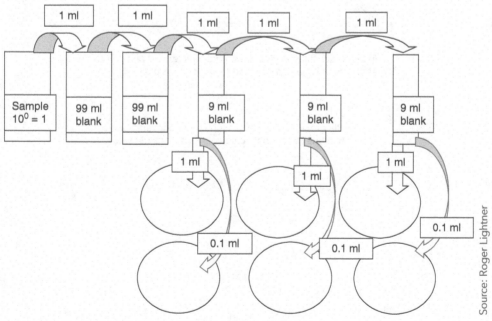

Schematic for Serial Dilution and Standard Plate Count

Exercise #2   Pour Plate Method

To perform the pour plate method, you will use the dilution tubes from the previous schematic and perform the top three agar plates. You will obtain three empty Petri dishes and label them with the dilution factors. Next, you will pipette 1 ml from each of the 9 ml dilution blanks into their respective plate. Lastly, you will obtain three molten Tryptic Soy Agar (TSA) agar tubes from the hot water bath and pour one agar tube into each plate. Swirl the agar to mix in the water and make the agar disperse evenly in the bottom of the plate. After the agar hardens, give the plates to the instructor for incubation. Next week you will notice that some of the colonies will be on top and grow larger while ones trapped down in the agar will be small and wedge shaped since they do not have as much freedom for growth.

DAY 2: RESULTS

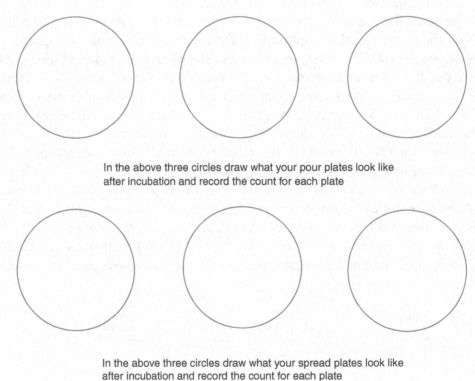

In the above three circles draw what your pour plates look like after incubation and record the count for each plate

In the above three circles draw what your spread plates look like after incubation and record the count for each plate

Record your final calculation for the concentration of bacteria in the original sample tube from last week

_____ bacterial cfus/ml

Source: Roger Lightner

1. Pipetting 1 ml into a 9-ml dilution blank results in a _____-fold dilution.

   a. 1
   b. 10
   c. 100
   d. 1,000

2. Pipetting 1 ml into a 99-ml dilution blank results in a _____-fold dilution.

   a. 1
   b. 10
   c. 100
   d. 1,000

3. Pipetting 0.1 ml from a dilution tube to an agar plate _____ change the dilution factor.

   a. will
   b. will not

4. If you pipette 0.1 ml from a dilution tube with a dilution factor of 10^{-3} onto an agar plate, then what will the dilution factor on the agar plate be?

   a. 10^{-2}
   b. 10^{-3}
   c. 10^{-4}
   d. 10^{-5}

5. If a tube has a dilution factor of 10^{-6}, then how many times more dilute is it than the original sample?

   a. two times
   b. 10 times
   c. 100 times
   d. 1,000 times
   e. one million times

6. What range of colonies constitutes a countable plate?

   a. 0–30
   b. 30–300
   c. 100–1,000
   d. 0–10,000

7. If a plate hypothetically has 750 colonies on it, you would:

   a. count it and record it as 750
   b. not count it and record it as TNTC
   c. not count it and record it as TFTC

8. If you had 250 colonies on a plate with a 10^{-4} dilution factor, then how would you record the final answer for the concentration in the original culture tube?

   a. 0.25×10^4
   b. 2.5×10^6
   c. 25×10^6
   d. 250×10^5

9. In order to get exactly 1 ml with a micropipetter, you push the plunger down to the:

   a. first stopping position
   b. second stopping position

10. If you spread the plates with the cell spreader in the order 10^{-6}, 10^{-7}, and 10^{-8}, then you would:

    a. need to flame it with burning alcohol between each plate
    b. only need to flame it one time with burning alcohol

8

Water Quality: Multiple Tube Fermentations and MPNs

DAY 1: MPN INOCULATION

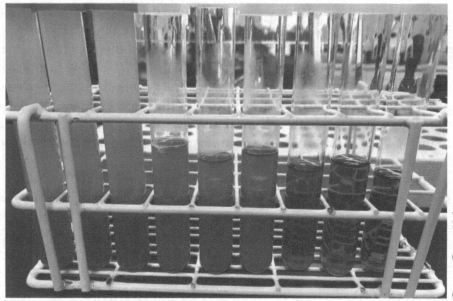

Source: Roger Lightner

The **Multiple Tube Fermentation Test,** also known as the **Most Probable Number (MPN)** method, is usually employed as a water quality test. This method identifies whether the water we have is safe to drink or use for other purposes, such as swimming or bathing. This test is primarily used to get a rough estimate of the number of coliform bacteria present in the water. The most famous coliform bacterium is *Escherichia coli.* You may hear on the news that water was tested and *E. coli* was present. This makes it sound like *E. coli* is a bad bacterium, but actually it is used as an indicator organism. **Coliforms** are defined as Gram-negative, rod-shaped bacteria that live in the intestines of warm-blooded animals and give off gas as they ferment lactose. So, if *E. coli* is present in water, it is an indicator that the water is contaminated with feces. If water contaminated with fecal material is consumed, it could also contain a number of intestinal pathogens such as Hepatitis A, *Salmonella,* Typhoid fever, cholera, or several other diarrheal diseases.

The standard for drinking water is zero. This means that there should not be any coliforms in the water for it to be considered clean enough to drink. If you see a sign that says **potable** water, it means the water is clean and safe to drink. Nonpotable water may not be clean enough to drink, but it may still be ok to bathe or swim in. Water you may see roped off at a lake for a swim area may have a few coliforms in it, but if the numbers get too high, it should be closed to swimming. Usually, a state agency is in charge of monitoring this.

The MPN method does not use any agar plates but rather is all done in test tubes. It is called the MPN because it is based on probability and statistics. This test utilizes a special broth to select for coliform bacteria called **Brilliant Green Lactose Bile (BGLB) broth**. Brilliant green is a pH indicator that will turn from dark green to more of a yellow-green as coliforms ferment the lactose sugar in the medium and produce acid. Lactose is a very difficult sugar to ferment and not many bacteria like it, but these bacteria are the ones that help warm-blooded animals that are fed on mother's milk to digest this dairy sugar. The bile helps select for intestinal bacteria that are used to its presence in the intestines coming from the liver. The tubes will also have the inverted Durham tubes to capture gas, which is an important part of the test. If coliform bacteria are growing in a BGLB broth tube, then the tube should turn yellow, have turbid growth, and possess a gas bubble. Only tubes with gas bubbles are counted as positive. Normally, an MPN test would use 15 tubes arranged in 3 sets of 5 tubes in each set per sample. For the sake of conserving test tubes and media, we will be using a nine-tube method to illustrate how the test works. A water sample is collected in a clean, sterile bottle. Next, the first three tubes will receive 10 ml each, the second set 1 ml each, and the third set 0.1 ml each. The probability of transferring a coliform bacterial cell from the bottle to a test tube decreases as the volume decreases. There is a relationship where the more bacteria present in the sample, the more positive tubes you will see following incubation. Also, you will notice that each volume has multiple replicates (in this case, three) performed at each volume. The diagram at the bottom of this page illustrates the schematic we will be using to inoculate the BGLB tubes.

Each test tube contains 8 ml of BGLB broth. The first set of tubes that receive 10 ml of water will dilute the nutrients in the broth; so to make sure that there are enough nutrients for any coliforms present, this broth is mixed up double strength or twice the normal strength (**dsBGLB**). The other tubes that are only getting 1 ml or 0.1 ml will not significantly dilute the broth, so it is mixed up at normal or single strength (**ssBGLB**).

After inoculation, the BGLB tubes are incubated for 48 hours at 37°C. Your instructor will save these tubes for you until the next lab period. When you read the tubes, any tube with a gas bubble is counted as positive and any tube without gas is considered negative. Next, you only count the positive tubes from each set to get your **combination of positives**. For example, if two out of three of the 10 ml tubes turned positive, one of the 1 ml tubes is positive, and none of the 0.1 ml tubes turned

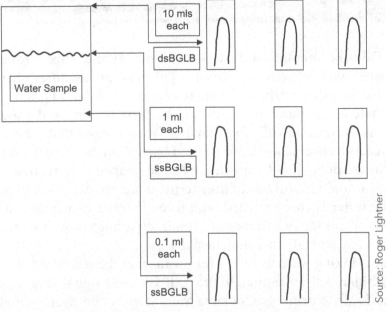

Schematic for MPN Test

Source: Roger Lightner

positive, then your combination of positives would be 2-1-0. The table starting on this page contains the statistical chart that statisticians have put together to calculate the MPN. Find the combination of positives on the table to get your final MPN answer per 100 ml of sample. If we look up our example combination of 2-1-0, you will see that the **MPN index** is 15. This means that the most likely number of coliforms that would give that result is about 15 coliform cells for every 100 ml of water.

Exercise #1   Inoculation of MPN Tubes

Procedure

- Obtain three dsBGLB tubes and label them for the 10 ml tubes.
- Obtain six ssBGLB tubes and label them for the 1 and 0.1 ml tubes.
- Your instructor will give you a fresh water sample to test.
- Shake the sample 30 times to thoroughly mix.
- Use a 10-ml serological pipette to transfer 10 ml of sample into each of the three 10 ml tubes.
- Now you can switch to a micropipetter to dispense 1 ml of sample into each of the 1 ml tubes.
- Adjust the micropipetter for 0.1 ml and use it to dispense 0.1 ml of sample into each of the 0.1 ml tubes.
- Place your nine inoculated tubes into the designated area for incubation and read the results next week.

Most Probable Number Table			
10 ml Tubes	**1 ml Tubes**	**0.1 ml Tubes**	**MPN/100 ml**
0	0	1	3
0	1	0	3
1	0	0	4
1	0	1	7
1	1	0	7
1	1	1	11
1	2	0	11
2	0	0	9
2	0	1	14
2	1	0	15
2	1	1	20
2	2	0	21
2	2	1	28
3	0	0	23
3	0	1	39

Continued

10 ml Tubes	1 ml Tubes	0.1 ml Tubes	MPN/100 ml
\multicolumn{4}{c}{Most Probable Number Table (*Continued*)}

10 ml Tubes	1 ml Tubes	0.1 ml Tubes	MPN/100 ml
3	0	2	64
3	1	0	43
3	1	1	75
3	1	2	120
3	2	0	93
3	2	1	150
3	2	2	210
3	3	0	240
3	3	1	460
3	3	2	1,100

DAY 2: RESULTS

Use the space below to record the number of positives you got for your MPN test. Next, look up the MPN for your number of positives in the table above and record the final MPN index here.

◖ Homework #8

1. What does the acronym MPN mean?

   a. Many Practical Numerals
   b. Most Probable Number
   c. Mostly Potable Numerically

2. What group of bacteria is the MPN test targeting?

   a. Gram-positive rods
   b. Gram-positive cocci
   c. coliforms
   d. Mycobacteria

3. What difficult sugar is being fermented during this test?

   a. glucose
   b. lactose
   c. mannitol
   d. arabinose

4. What happens to Brilliant green pH indicator when acid is produced?

   a. it turns yellow
   b. it turns purple
   c. it turns pink

5. What must be present in order to consider the tube to be a positive reaction?

   a. it must turn pink
   b. it must turn yellow
   c. it must have a gas bubble

6. Which set of tubes has dsBGLB broth in them?

   a. 10 ml tubes
   b. 1 ml tubes
   c. 0.1 ml tubes
   d. all of the above

7. If all nine test tubes turn positive, then what would the combination of positives be?

   a. 0-0-0
   b. 1-1-1
   c. 3-3-3
   d. 9-9-9

8. If you get a combination of positives of 3-1-0, then what would the MPN index be?

   a. 7
   b. 11
   c. 23
   d. 43

9. What is the MPN standard for drinking water?
   a. zero
   b. 20
   c. 40
   d. 1,100

10. Potable water means that the water is:
   a. safe enough to drink
   b. safe enough to swim in but not safe to drink

LAB WEEK

9

Microbial Control: Disinfectants, Antibiotics, and UV Light

DAY 1: DISINFECTANT, ANTIBIOTIC AND UV LIGHT SETUP

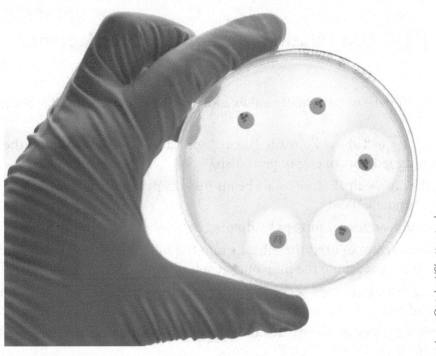

Jarun Ontakrai/Shutterstock.com

Earlier in the semester we discussed environmental factors that affect the growth of living organsms. With microbial control, we studied how to limit their growth or kill them to protect ourselves from disease or infection. Sometimes we attack microbes with chemicals and sometimes physically. The first exercise today is to test the effectiveness of disinfectants. A **disinfectant** is a harsh chemical that kills microbes and should only be used on inanimate objects because it is strong enough to kill human tissue as well. **Antiseptics** are mild enough to use on living tissue and include solutions such as rubbing alcohol or hydrogen peroxide. This test could be performed on any solution or brand, but we will test three popular disinfectants today. There have been many TV commercials for Lysol and Pinesol claiming that one is better than the other, so we can see what our test shows this week. It is becoming more common today to hear that there are environmentally friendly cleaners we can use that are just as effective but don't expose us to the harsh chemicals of traditional brands. We will test one of the most well-known environmental cleaners called Simple Green to see if it really is as effective.

It will take the entire class working as a group to cover all of the solutions in this lab. Since a chemical may kill one type of bacterium better than another, we usually test them against both Gram positives and Gram negatives to see how effective they are. There are six lab benches in the room. Three benches on one side will test against *E. coli*, which is a Gram-negative bacterium. The other side will use the Gram-positive bacterium *Staphylococcus epidermidis*. The front row will test Lysol, the second row will use Pinesol, and the back row will use Simple Green. In this way, each disinfectant is tested against both types of bacteria. The method we are using today is called the **use dilution method**. It is designed to test the solutions like you would use them in your home at various dilutions. For example, you may use a concentrated cleaner right out of the bottle for countertops but dilute it down to make mop water. The Center for Disease Control (CDC) uses a 10% bleach solution to disinfect biohazard suites. Many disinfectants will give directions for mop water to mix one-quarter cup of disinfectant with one gallon of water. This comes out to a 1:64 dilution. We will test each disinfectant at three dilutions, including full strength, 10%, and the 1:64 mop bucket concentration. You will also see that each solution is tested in triplicate. If done only once, the results might be a fluke, but if you get the same results with three replicates, you feel much more confident about the results.

Exercise #1   Use Dilution Method for Disinfectants

Procedure

- Use the figure on page 61 to visually follow along with these stepwise directions to perform this exercise.
- The supplies you need should already be on your table. Start by dumping the bacterial culture your table is assigned into an empty petri dish.
- Next, dump the tube with 12 sterile glass beads into the petri dish and swirl them into the bacterial culture to contaminate them.
- Sterilize a pair of tweezers or forceps by dipping in alcohol and flaming them off.
- Use the sterile tweezers to drop three beads into the full strength tube, three beads into the 10% solution, and three beads into the mop bucket solution.
- The remaining three beads will serve as positive controls to show that the culture is not killed by water alone and will grow in the culture medium used later.
- Start a 10-minute timer to allow a 10-minute exposure to the disinfectant, which is what many disinfectant labels contain on their directions.
- After 10 minutes, you can dump the disinfectant tubes each into a clean, sterile petri dish. This is to make it easier to pick the beads up with tweezers.
- Since we do not know which beads have live bacteria on them, you have to flame off the tweezers before picking up each bead.
- You will now need 12 prelabeled Tryptic Soy Broth (TSB) tubes. The labels should show the disinfectant and the concentration the bead was exposed to.
- Use the tweezers to drop one bead into each of the 12 TSB tubes, flaming the tweezers between each bead.
- The TSB tubes will be incubated until the following period, and if any bacteria survive their exposure, there will be growth in the broth. If the tube shows no growth, this means that the 10-minute exposure to that concentration of disinfectant killed all of the bacteria.

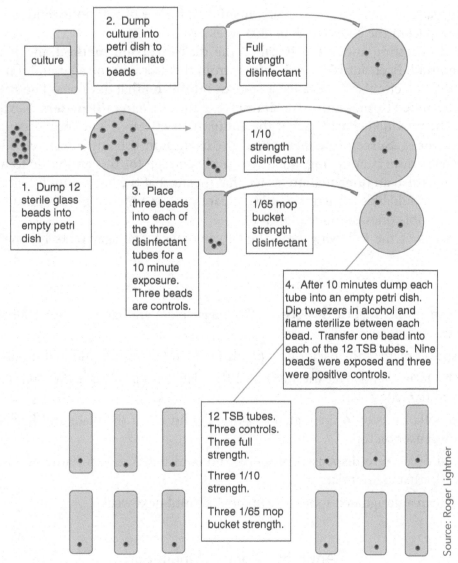

2. Dump culture into petri dish to contaminate beads

culture

Full strength disinfectant

1. Dump 12 sterile glass beads into empty petri dish

1/10 strength disinfectant

3. Place three beads into each of the three disinfectant tubes for a 10 minute exposure. Three beads are controls.

1/65 mop bucket strength disinfectant

4. After 10 minutes dump each tube into an empty petri dish. Dip tweezers in alcohol and flame sterilize between each bead. Transfer one bead into each of the 12 TSB tubes. Nine beads were exposed and three were positive controls.

12 TSB tubes. Three controls. Three full strength.

Three 1/10 strength.

Three 1/65 mop bucket strength.

Source: Roger Lightner

Use Dilution Method for Disinfectants

Exercise #2   Antibiotics

Antibiotics are secretions from living organisms, such as bacteria and fungi, that are antibacterial in their nature. This means that antibiotics are used to treat bacterial infections but are not effective against other microbes like viruses and fungi. Like disinfectants, it is possible that an antibiotic may kill one type of bacterium but not another so they will be tested against both. For example, penicillin is only effective against Gram positives and polymyxin B is better against Gram negatives.

Antibiotics target one part of the bacterial prokaryotic cell. There are five recognized **modes of action**. Some antibiotics like penicillin attack the peptidoglycan cell wall. Polymyxin B targets the cell membrane. Erythromycin is one of many well-known antibiotics that attack the ribosomes to prevent protein synthesis. Some antibiotics like Cipro target the nucleic acids, and some, like sulfa drugs, slow down bacterial growth by hindering metabolic pathways.

This lab will also take the entire class working together as a group to cover all of the scenarios. Each table will be assigned one organism to make a spread plate from. There will be three Gram-positive bacteria used and three Gram negatives. Antibiotic disks will be dispensed on top of each spread plate with an automatic device. There will be six to eight antibiotics of various modes of action used. The strategy is to expose a variety of organisms to a variety of antibiotics and see if there are any trends that develop from the collected data next week.

This method of testing antibiotics is called the **disk-diffusion method** and is also called the **Kirby-Bauer method**. Each antibiotic will diffuse from the disk into the agar and if it kills the bacteria, then there will be a circular zone called a **zone of inhibition** that develops. The size of the zone of inhibition is determined by measuring the **diameter** of the circle in **millimeters**. Next, this size value is compared to the provided chart to see if the antibiotic is effective. The measurement can fall into one of three categories. **Susceptible** means that the bacterium is being effectively killed. **Resistant** means that the bacterium is not being killed effectively enough for this antibiotic to work if given to the patient. There is also an **intermediate** range that means that the bacterium is being killed but not as effectively as we would like. Sometimes intermediately susceptible antibiotics must be used because more highly susceptible ones cannot be found.

Follow the steps of the following procedure to inoculate one agar plate for the disk-diffusion method.

Procedure

- Obtain a clean sterile **Tryptic Soy Agar** (TSA) agar plate and label it with your initials and the organism assigned to your table.
- Perform a spread plate of the bacteria by pipetting 0.1 ml of your liquid culture on the plate.
- Spread the bacteria evenly over the surface of the plate with a cell spreader that has been dipped in alcohol and flamed.
- Put the antibiotic disks onto the plate by taking the lid off of the plate and firmly stamping the automatic dispenser on top.
- Make sure all disks were dispensed properly and land flat. You can flame off tweezers to push down any disks that are not flat.
- Place the plate in a designated spot to be incubated until next week.

Antibiotic Zones of Inhibition

Antibiotic	Resistant	Intermediate	Susceptible
Ampicillin – *E. coli*	≤13	14–16	≥17
Ampicillin – *Staphylococcus*	≤28		≥29
Amoxicillin – *Staphylococcus*	≤19		≥20
Amoxicillin – other	≤13	14–17	≥18
Bacitracin	≤8	9–12	≥13
Chloramphenicol	≤12	13–17	≥18
Erythromycin	≤13	14–22	≥23
Neomycin	≤12	13–16	≥17
Penicillin – *E. coli*	≤14		≥15

Continued

Antibiotic	Resistant	Intermediate	Susceptible
Penicillin – *Staphylococcus*	≤28		≥29
Polymyxin B	≤8	9–11	≥12
Streptomycin	≤14	15–20	≥21
Sulfasoxazole	≤12	13–16	≥17
Tetracycline	≤14	15–18	≥19
Trimethoprim	≤10	11–15	≥16
Vancomycin	≤9	10–11	≥12

Exercise #3 Ultraviolet Light as a Control Agent

One physical way to control microbial growth is to bombard them with radiation. **Ultraviolet (UV)** radiation is detrimental to living organisms because it causes damage to their DNA. UV light is being used as a safer alternative to some of the traditional chemicals we use, especially chlorine gas. One drawback of UV light is that it does not penetrate items well and only cleans surfaces. If you are wanting to disinfect hard surfaces though, UV light can be used in a safe, effective manner.

Today, we are going to test several different species of bacteria to see how long of an intense UV light exposure they can withstand before being killed off at a high percentage. We will use the same culture you used for the antibiotic plate to perform this test. The culture will be in liquid form so you can make spread plates. After the bacterium is applied, you will take your plates to the UV light hood and each one will be exposed for a different length of time. You will have to take the plastic lid off of the plate during exposure because the UV light will not penetrate through it.

The next procedure will walk you step by step on how to perform this test. Next, week you will record the results in the following table using the −, +, ++, +++ system to illustrate how much remaining bacteria is left surviving on the plate.

Procedure

- Obtain six sterile TSA agar plates and label them with your initials and the length of exposure in seconds to the UV light. The six exposure times are 0 (control plate), 30, 60, 90, 120, and 180 seconds.
- Use micropipetter to dispense 0.1 ml of the culture onto each plate.
- Make a spread plate by spreading the surface of the plate evenly with a cell spreader that has been dipped in alcohol and flamed.
- Have your instructor escort you to the UV light hood. Take with you a pair of gloves, goggles, and your cell phone to set a stopwatch.
- Leave the control plate out because it will not be exposed to show that the plate will have a solid growth of bacteria with no UV light exposure.
- Place the other five plates into the hood and remove the lids.

- Start your stopwatch and when you get to the time indicated for each plate, replace the lid and remove it from the hood. The first plate removed will be the 30-second plate and the last one removed will be the 180-second plate.
- Return the plates to the designated area for incubation until next week and then record the results in the table located in the results section.

DAY 2: RESULTS

During this second lab period, you will look at the TSB tubes and record the results for the entire class in the following table. We will use a (+) to indicate that there was growth and therefore the bacterium was not completely killed by that concentration of disinfectant. We will use a (–) to show that the bacteria were all killed. The positive control tubes should all three be positive. This shows that the organism should be alive and grow because water alone does not kill it off. If your control tubes are not all three positive, then a mistake was made that would invalidate all of your data.

Results for Use Dilution Method

Organism Used	Disinfectant	Dilution Used	Number of Positives	Use Dilution
E. coli (G—)	Lysol	Control		
		Full strength		
		10%		
		Mop bucket		
	Pinesol	Control		
		Full strength		
		10%		
		Mop bucket		
	Simple Green	Control		
		Full strength		
		10%		
		Mop bucket		
Staphylococcus epidermidis (G+)	Lysol	Control		
		Full strength		
		10%		
		Mop bucket		
	Pinesol	Control		
		Full strength		
		10%		

Continued

Organism Used	Disinfectant	Dilution Used	Number of Positives	Use Dilution
		Mop bucket		
	Simple Green	Control		
		Full strength		
		10%		
		Mop bucket		

During this second week of the lab, you will receive a ruler to measure the size of the zones of inhibition. Record the values as diameter in millimeters in the following table. Compare each value to the antibiotic table on the page 62 and rank each one as being resistant, intermediate, or susceptible. The instructor will give you the data that the entire class has generated. Lastly, the instructor will tell you some typical trends that are seen in the medical field. Look to see if your data support these trends.

Results for the Antibiotic Disk-Diffusion Method

Mode of Action								
Organism Used								

Results of UV Light Exposure

Pet Letter	0″ Control	30″	60″	90″	120″	180″

1. What are disinfectants used on?

    a. living tissue
    b. inanimate objects only

2. What is the solid contaminated surface we are using in this lab?

    a. test tubes
    b. Petri dishes
    c. glass beads

3. What is the exposure time for the disinfectants?

    a. 30 seconds
    b. 1 minute
    c. 3 minutes
    d. 10 minutes

4. If the disinfectant killed the bacteria, then the TSB tube should be:

    a. positive
    b. negative

5. Antibiotics work against which types of microbes?

    a. bacteria
    b. viruses
    c. fungi
    d. all of the above

6. Which group of organisms should penicillin work best against?

    a. Gram positives
    b. Gram negatives

7. What is the target of the cell if an antibiotic inhibits protein synthesis?

    a. cell wall
    b. cell membrane
    c. ribosomes
    d. PABA

8. The size of zones of inhibitions is expressed as:

    a. area in cm^2
    b. circumference in cm
    c. radius in inches
    d. diameter in mm

9. What does UV light damage in living cells?
   a. cell walls
   b. cell membranes
   c. DNA
   d. mitochondria

10. What drawback or limitation does UV light have as a microbial control method?
    a. it does not kill but only slows growth
    b. it is very expensive
    c. it is highly toxic and requires evacuation strategies for safety
    d. it does not penetrate well so is limited to surfaces

10

Immunology I: Blood Typing and White Blood Cell Counts

DAY 1: BLOOD TYPING AND WHITE BLOOD CELL COUNT

Ikordela/Shutterstock.com

    Immunology is the study of how the immune system works. The immune system functions by producing little protein molecules called **antibodies** that respond to small protein molecules on the surface of cells called **antigens**. Antigens come in over a billion shapes, and each antibody is specific for one of these shapes so they match uniquely like matching puzzle pieces. Antibodies are Y-shaped so that they have **two antigen binding sites,** allowing for them to bind to more than one molecule. Because of this unique property, antibodies that are known for what antigen they are specific for can be produced and then used as a diagnostic tool. This field is sometimes called **serology** because the antibodies come from blood serum.

    One of the most famous immunological tests is the one used to determine blood type. The first part of a blood type is called the **ABO blood group**. It gets its name because there are three alleles for this gene. The A-gene codes for a protein called the **A-antigen** that will be present on the red blood cells if a person has this gene. The B-gene likewise codes for a **B-antigen** that would be present on the red blood cells if that gene is present. The O-gene does not code any protein so you can think of it as a zero because there is nothing there. You may have learned about genetics in another class and that humans are diploid, so we possess two copies of most of our genes. We inherited one copy from our mother and the other copy from our father. Also, the A-gene and B-gene are both **dominant,** while the O-gene is a **recessive** trait. There are numerous possible combinations. The following table summarizes what blood types are associated with each possible allele combination.

Relationship of Allele Combinations to Blood Type

Possible Allele Combinations	Individual's Blood Type
$I^A I^A$ or $I^A i$	Type A
$I^B I^B$ or $I^B i$	Type B
$I^A I^B$	Type AB
ii	Type O

The symbol for the A-allele is (I^A), and the upper case letter shows that it is a dominant trait. Likewise, the symbol for the B-allele is (I^B), which is also dominant. The symbol for the O-allele is (i), and the lower case letter indicates that it is a recessive trait. So, to have type O blood, a person must be homozygous recessive. With blood type, we also see that type AB blood results because the person has two dominant traits that are both expressed equally in what is called **codominance**.

The second part of blood typing is the **Rh factor**. If a person has a protein on their red blood cells called the **Rh-antigen,** then they have positive blood. If a person is lacking the Rh-antigen, then they have negative blood. The Rh-antigen is controlled by a separate gene from the ABO blood group. If a person is **homozygous dominant** (RR) or **heterozygous** (Rr), then they have positive blood. Negative blood type occurs when a person is **homozygous recessive** (rr). The following diagram illustrates what antigens must be present to determine each blood type.

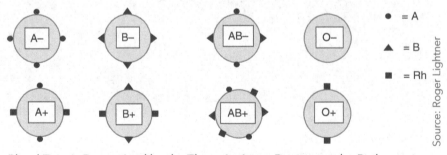

Blood Type Is Determined by the Three Antigens Present on the Red Blood Cells

Blood type is determined by the presence or absence of antigens A and B on the red blood cells. If a cell has the A-antigen, then it will be type A blood. If the cell has the B-antigen, then it will be type B blood. If both of these antigens are present, then the blood type is AB. If the Rh-antigen is present, then the blood will be a positive type. Notice on the diagram that AB⁺ blood has all three antigens and type O⁻ blood is lacking all three. One way to remember which blood types you can receive in a blood transfusion is that "you cannot receive an antigen you do not have." For example, if you have type A⁻ blood, then you have the A-antigen and not the B-antigen or the Rh-antigen. Therefore, you cannot receive any blood with these antigens on it and are limited to A⁻ and O⁻ in a transfusion. Type AB⁺

blood is **universal recipient** because it has all three antigens and will not reject them. Type O⁻ blood is **universal donor** because there are no antigens on the cell to reject.

Blood typing can also be used as part of a paternity test. Remember that during meiosis when sperm and eggs are produced, each sperm or egg will only get one of the alleles from the parent diploid cell. To figure out what possible blood types a child can have, we can use Punnett squares. The following Punnett square shows an example of how a man could be ruled out.

Punnett Square

	I^A	I^B
i	$I^A i$	$I^B i$
i	$I^A i$	$I^B i$

In this example, one parent is type O and the other is type AB. This results in a 50% chance of a child being type A and 50% chance of being type B. Notice that if the type AB parent is the father, it is not possible for them to have a type O child so he could be ruled out during a paternity test.

Next, we need to discuss how the blood typing test works. Each sample of blood needs to be tested separately for each of the three antigens. This is done using antibodies that are specific for each antigen. We can use a slide that has three wells on it and add a couple of drops of blood into each well. In the first well, you mix an anti-A antibody into the blood; if the blood has the A-antigen, the blood and antibody will clump together in what is called an **agglutination** reaction. Since each antibody has two binding sites, it can stick to the two red blood cells simultaneously. As they stick together, the clumps become heavy enough to precipitate out of the reaction. In the second well, you mix the blood with an anti-B antibody and in the third well with an anti-Rh antibody. If the antigen is not present on the blood cells, the clumping reaction does not occur. The picture on the first page of this lab shows what an agglutination reaction looks like. The following figure illustrates that the agglutination reaction occurs because the antibody has two antigen binding sites.

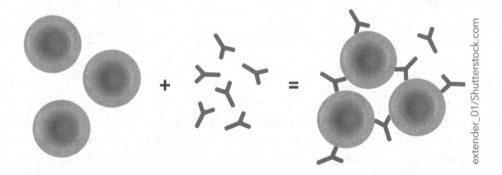

extender_01/Shutterstock.com

Exercise #1   Blood Typing

Procedure

- Each person will be provided an unknown blood sample (artificial blood will be used for safety so no one is exposed to potential pathogens). Record the identification number of your sample.
- Obtain a blood typing slide that has three wells on it.

- Place two drops of blood into each well.
- Place two drops of anti-A antibody into the A well.
- Place two drops of anti-B antibody into the B well.
- Place two drops of anti-Rh antibody in the Rh well.
- Stir each well with a separate toothpick to prevent cross-contamination.
- After a couple of minutes, observe which wells agglutinated to determine the blood type. For example, if you see clumping in the A well and Rh well but not in the B well, then the person is A^+. If a person is AB^+, they would clump in all three and O^- does not clump in any of the wells.

White blood cells (WBCs) are more technically called **leukocytes**. WBCs are involved in immunity such as when phagocytic cells engulf invading pathogens to fight against infection. Leukocytes are identified by the appearance of their nucleus and whether or not they have any granules in the cell that makes it look polka-dotted in the microscope. The following table presents a summary of the five major types of WBCs, their proportions, and their functions.

White Blood Cell Distribution and Function

WBC	Normal Percentages	Function
Granulocytes		
Basophils	~1	Inflammation
Eosinophils	2–5	Attack large parasites
Neutrophils	60–65	Phagocytic
Agranulocytes		
Monocytes	5–8	Phagocytic
Lymphocytes	25–30	Antibody production

You will notice from this table that the neutrophils and the monocytes are **phagocytic**. Lymphocytes are important in the **adaptive immune response** producing antibodies against specific antigens. As you look at a blood slide, you will observe that the percentages of neutrophils and lymphocytes are higher. There are some rules on how to identify each leukocyte. The following diagram shows microscope pictures of each one to help you see what you will be looking for. Basophils will be heavily granulated with dark purple granules. The granules of eosinophils will be red and the nucleus is bilobed. Neutrophils are easily spotted because of their funny shaped, multilobed nuclei. This is why neutrophils are also known as **polymorphonuclear leukocytes (PMNLs or PMNs)**. Monocytes will be very large and smooth looking with a large nucleus that probably looks like a kidney bean. These monocytes will probably be four or five times larger than the red blood cells around them. Lymphocytes will have a round nucleus that takes up most of the cell with very little cytoplasm. They are also very small, being about the size of the red blood cells around them.

Leukocyte series

Agranular   ## Granular

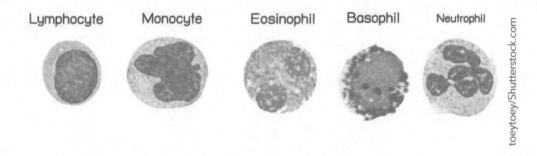

Lymphocyte   Monocyte   Eosinophil   Basophil   Neutrophil

toeytoey/Shutterstock.com

Exercise #2   Differential White Blood Cell Count

Procedure

- Obtain a prepared blood slide that has already been stained.
- Focus on the slide in the microscope going all the way up to oil immersion.
- As you observe the slide, set the mechanical stage so that you can move back and forth across the slide and will not be seeing the same cells more than one time.
- Begin looking and moving to identify the WBCs as you go. There will only be a few in view at any one time.
- Use the following table to take a tally of each type of cell. Keep counting until you have seen 100 leukocytes.
- Now look at the percentages of what you observed and compare them to the earlier table.
- Do any of the cell percentages look far out of place? Remember that basophils are very low percentage and you will be lucky to see one and you may only see a couple of eosinophils.
- Hematologists can get an idea of what type of infection a person may have. For example, a person with a bacterial infection may have an elevated neutrophil count, while a viral infection may have an elevated lymphocyte count.

DAY 1: RESULTS

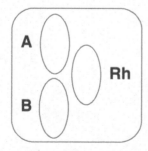

A

B

Rh

Use this figure to make a drawing of what your patient's blood
typing slide looked like and record the final interpretation beside

White Blood Cell Tally

Basophils	
Eosinophils	
Neutrophils	
Monocytes	
Lymphocytes	

1. If a person has only the A-antigen on their red blood cells, what blood type will they have?

    a. Type A⁻
    b. Type A⁺
    c. Type B⁺
    d. Type O⁻

2. Which of the following blood types is a dominant trait?

    a. Type A
    b. Type O

3. If a person has a genotype of $I^B i$, what blood type will they have?

    a. Type A
    b. Type B
    c. Type O

4. To have type O blood, you must be:

    a. homozygous dominant
    b. homozygous recessive
    c. heterozygous

5. The presence of which antigen determines that the blood is positive?

    a. A-antigen
    b. B-antigen
    c. Rh-antigen

6. If a person has type B⁺ blood, which of the following blood types would they not be able to receive in a blood transfusion?

    a. B⁻
    b. B⁺
    c. AB⁺
    d. O⁻

7. How many antigen binding sites does each antibody have?

    a. only one
    b. two for each Y-shaped molecule

8. The clumping reaction seen during a blood typing test is called:

    a. a hematocrit
    b. a cross reaction
    c. agglutination

9. Perform a Punnett square to see what percentage of the offspring will be type O if one parent has a genotype of I^Ai and the other parent is I^Bi.

    a. 0%
    b. 25%
    c. 50%
    d. 75%
    e. 100%

10. If you perform a blood typing test and there is clumping in the B well but not in the A well or the Rh well, then the person is:

    a. A^+
    b. B^-
    c. AB^-
    d. O^+

Immunology II: ELISA

DAY 1: ELISA TESTING

cawee/Shutterstock.com

ELISA is an acronym that stands for **Enzyme-Linked Immunosorbent Assay**. This is another immunologically based diagnostic test that uses the properties of antibodies to diagnose disease. ELISAs have become a widely used test to identify many things, but probably the most famous one is the first step in identifying if a person is HIV positive. The test we do today will simulate this. There are no dangerous chemicals or agents, it uses plant-based compounds to do the simulation.

There are two strategies of the ELISA test: direct ELISA and indirect ELISA. Today we will do the **indirect ELISA**, which means we will not directly detect whether a patient has HIV infection. Rather, we will indirectly determine whether the person has HIV infection by detecting whether the person has antibodies against the virus in their blood.

The first step of the indirect ELISA is to use plastic plates, called **microtiter plates,** with very small wells. The experiment is performed in **triplicate** to allow more confidence about the results and rule out the possibility of a false-positive or false-negative test due to experimental error. Each well on the plate will have HIV antigens imbedded into the plastic sides. Next, you fill three of the wells with the patient's blood serum. Then, run both positive and negative controls to make sure that the procedure and reagents are all working properly. After the serum sits for a little bit to allow for any antibodies to attach to the viral antigens, perform the first wash. If the patient has antibodies, the serum will stick to the sides of the well. If a patient is negative and there are no antibodies present, then the well remains clean.

The second step is to add an antibody to detect human antibodies. This is done by taking the human protein and putting it into an animal like a rabbit. The rabbit will produce an antibody called **anti-human antibody**. This molecule also has a specific enzyme attached or linked to it. An enzyme that causes a color change is usually chosen. The enzyme used in this test will turn a particular plant substrate brown so we will see a brown color in the positive reactions. Each well is filled with an enzyme-linked anti-human antibody. If the human HIV antibody is present, then the anti-human antibody will stick to the sides of the well. If there is no human HIV antibody present, then there is nothing for the anti-human antibody to stick to and it washes away during the second wash.

The final step is to fill the washed wells with a solution containing the substrate that is specific for that enzyme. If the enzyme is present, the well will turn brown after a short incubation period. A positive test means that the enzyme is present and that the HIV antibody must also be present or it would have washed away. The negative control wells should be colorless because it did wash away. The positive controls should be brown to indicate what a positive test looks like. Compare your unknown patient sample to determine whether your patient is HIV positive or not. The following diagram shows what the molecules will look like inside the well, allowing for a positive reaction to occur.

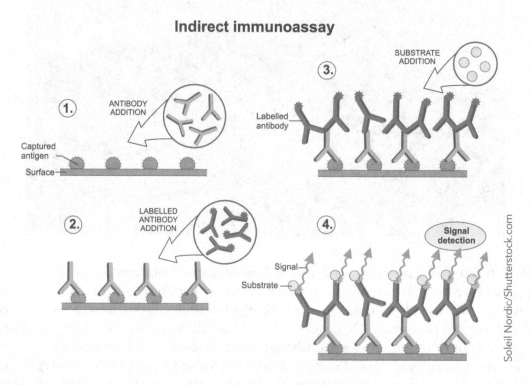

Indirect immunoassay

Exercise #1   Indirect ELISA for HIV Testing

Procedure

The specific steps and instructions can vary according to the brand of ELISA kit we will be using. The exact step-by-step procedure will be provided by the instructor on the day of the lab.

DAY 1: RESULTS

Use the space below to draw what your microtiter plate looks like and the results you got for each sample.

1. Which ELISA strategy is usually the first step in diagnosing a patient as HIV positive?

   a. direct ELISA
   b. indirect ELISA

2. Which ELISA strategy detects the presence of HIV (virus particles) in the patient's serum?

   a. direct ELISA
   b. indirect ELISA

3. Which antibody will have the enzyme linked to it?

   a. first antibody from patient serum
   b. second antibody (anti-human)

4. What happened to the enzyme if an ELISA test is negative?

   a. it was denatured by the incubation temperature
   b. it was on the wrong antibody and did not stick to the sides of the well
   c. there was no patient antibody present, so there was nothing for the linked antibody to stick to

5. In which type of person will the first antibody be present that will stick to the sides of the well?

   a. HIV positive
   b. HIV negative

6. What color will the negative control wells be after performing the test?

   a. colorless
   b. brown

7. What color will the positive control wells be after performing the test?

   a. colorless
   b. brown

8. How many times, ideally, should each sample be run?

   a. it only needs to be run once
   b. duplicate
   c. triplicate

9. If the negative control wells change color, then what probably happened?

   a. there was cross contamination from a positive well or micropipette
   b. the reagents are defective
   c. the first antibody is expired
   d. the second antibody is expired

10. What should you do if the negative controls turn color?

    a. repeat the experiment and be more careful
    b. diagnose the patient as HIV positive
    c. report the patient as being HIV negative